SILENCE AT RAMSCLIFFE

SILENCE AT RAMSCLIFFE
Foot and Mouth in Devon

Photography and Text
Chris Chapman

Poetry
James Crowden

B

THE BARDWELL PRESS

Page 2: The silage clamp cleaned and disinfected, Ramscliffe Farm, Beaford, North Devon

Text and Photographs © 2005 Chris Chapman (unless otherwise stated)
Poems © 2005 James Crowden
Foreword © 2005 Carol Trewin
Permission to reproduce extracts from *A Manufactured Plague* kindly granted by Abigail Woods and Earthscan, © 2004 Abigail Woods.
Permission for use of the film *Silence at Ramscliffe* kindly given by ITV West. © itv 2005

Published by:

The Bardwell Press
6 Bardwell Road
Oxford OX2 6SW
www.bardwell-press.co.uk

British Library Cataloguing in Publication Data
A catalogue record for this book is available from the British Library

ISBN 0-9548683-3-1

Designed and Typeset by The Bardwell Press, Oxford.
Printed in Italy by EBS Verona

CONTENTS

ACKNOWLEDGEMENTS

In the Spring of 2001 Foot and Mouth Disease came upon us unexpectedly and caused an enormous amount of anguish and grief to many of our friends. But a crisis brings out stoicism in people and highlights the qualities that caused them to be your friends in the first place. The authors would like to thank the following: The Mudge family at Huccaby, Derek and Gwen Mortimore, the Hardings at Wonson, Colin and Hazel Pearse, Simon Timms, Stephen Bond, Dennis Bater, Ron Dawson, Kate Ruscombe-King, Chris Vile, David Parker, Carol Trewin, Terry Ward, Jennie Hayes, Chris Fogg and Robert Kilby.

We also owe an enormous debt to Devon County Council and Beaford Arts and especially to Philip, Percy and Roma Lake for their welcome at Ramscliffe and their help in the documentation of events.

Grateful thanks are due to the following sponsors without whom this book would not have been possible:

Devon County Council
Dartmoor National Park Authority
West Devon Borough Council
The Dartmoor Society
CLA (Country Land and Business Association)
National Farmers' Union (South West Region)
The Fishleigh Estate
Strutt & Parker, Exeter Office
Barramoor Farm, North Bovey
Little Ash Organic Farm, Whiddon Down
Moorlands Farm Shop, Whiddon Down
Gillhouse Farm, Zeal Monachorum
Okeford Veterinary Centre, Okehampton
Greyface Dartmoor Sheep Breeder: Higher Haye 640
The Mid Devon Foxhounds
Videotel Productions Ltd
Focal Point
NWM Brand Development
The Almonds Ltd
Canns Down Press Ltd, Beaford
Littoral Arts Trust
Tim Russ
Paul and Kay Henderson (founding directors of
    Gidleigh Park)
Anne Voss-Bark, The Arundell Arms, Lifton
Gravetye Manor
Tony and Pauline Pearce

Tony Garner, Shawlands Farm, Lingfield, Surrey
The Public Speaking Group
Capt. Guy Crowden
Squadron Leader Frank Chapman
Hugo de Ferranti
Tom Magnier
Jim Hindson
Moorhaven, Ivybridge
Julyan and Felicity Capper
Liz and Bill Pybus
John and Linda Larson
Charles and Kären Abbe
Gill and Peter Cave, Friars Hele, Meeth
Mike and Jennie Dunse, Bridestowe
Moorland Builders Ltd
Monks Withecombe Gallery
Super Audio Mastering
ITV West
EMI Music
Digitalcut
Available Light Productions Ltd
Mole Avon Town & Country Stores, Okehampton
Mary Critchley, www.warmwell.com
Jane and Michael Niven
John and Marilyn Daw
Mole Valley Farmers Ltd, South Molton
Rendells—Auctioneers, Valuers and Estate Agents
Nicky Scott—Composting for All
COCOON—felt burial shrouds
The Ecologist—Zac Goldsmith

The spring and summer of 2001 were terrible times for British farmers. Across the whole country, but more particularly in Devon, Cumbria, Dumfries and Galloway, the terror and emotional turmoil of the worst outbreak of animal disease in living memory changed lives for ever. Even though there was no risk to human health—unlike BSE, which has to date claimed just over 180,000 cattle lives and posed potential threats to humans—the Foot and Mouth epidemic led to the mainly unnecessary destruction of millions of pigs, cattle, sheep, goats, lambs, calves and piglets, and had a profound impact on farming and hundreds of other rural businesses.

The events of that spring were also the first real test of Tony Blair's government, four years after his first election victory. Faced with an imminent election, driven by his personal desire to make his mark in British political history by winning a second consecutive term for Labour, Blair personally took control of the crisis. He failed that test, as this book painfully illustrates.

FOREWORD

Chris Chapman and James Crowden are both deeply rooted in the countryside. One a photographer, the other a poet, they have both earned their living through observing rural life at every level, from the rawness of lambing on open downland in freezing, blizzard conditions to recording the end of generations of one farming family's history. They bring a new, human perspective to a crisis that, as Chris's personal account, his pictures and James's poetry reveal, was made infinitely worse by crucial decisions made by government ministers, scientists and others with a vested interest, none of whom had any understanding of the mayhem and emotional turmoil this would cause.

Not only do Chris and James acutely observe and understand the agony and despair experienced on hundreds of farms across Britain, they also show with clarity how politicians, bureaucrats and Whitehall mandarins had no understanding of the long term consequences of their actions, of the rhythms of rural life, of the seasons or the close links between farming and other rural businesses, or that many rural businesses would suffer far more hardship than those farms directly infected by the disease.

This record of those events of 2001 is an important document. While for many of those affected the memories are still too painful to recall, it is important for the rest of us to understand that this was a series of events largely outside the control of most of the farming industry. Foot and Mouth Disease swooped down on British farms largely out of the blue, unseen until it was too late, and extended its devastating grip to more than 2,000 farms. It cannot be argued that British agriculture was totally blameless, but until the disease appeared it could be argued that too many officials who should have known better were looking the wrong way. Farmers, and other rural businesses, ended up the political pawns in a much bigger game played by politicians, food manufacturers, vets and scientists.

Silence at Ramscliffe offers an alternative view of what really happened, a fresh insight and a better understanding of the irrevocable, long-term effects that this epidemic had on Britain's countryside. This is a poignant record that will survive long after all the official reports have been buried in dusty, Whitehall archives.

Each time I read these poems, or watch Chris and James relive their experiences by recounting these events to an audience, I have the same reaction—a mixture of pain, horror and sadness. Familiarity does not lessen these emotions.

It was Rudyard Kipling who wrote the words "lest we forget". The impact of the events of 2001 on Chris and James has left its mark too, and this is their contribution to make sure that we do not forget, and that the 2001 FMD epidemic is not consigned to the dustbin of forgotten history.

© Carol Trewin, Horrabridge, April 2005
For eleven years Carol Trewin worked for the BBC and was editor of Farming Today. *She was also farming editor of the* Western Morning News *and later joined* Taste of the West *in Cornwall. She writes on food, farming and the countryside for many publications. In 1999 she was elected an associate of the Royal Agricultural Society of England.*

Most of us, if old enough, can remember where we were when J F Kennedy was shot, or what we were doing on the day the Twin Towers were wiped off the face of Manhattan. They are personal memories and may seem insignificant, but they have attached themselves to these historic events and can bring them back in an instant. Other memories run deeper and unfold at a slower pace. Although it is forty years ago, I can still recall watching the state funeral of Winston Churchill on a black and white television. After days of sombre bulletins it was announced that the great man was dead and as the cortege progressed up the Thames, my mother and paternal grandmother, who were never on the friendliest of terms, found themselves sat in the same room, calm now with their hands in their laps, staring sadly at the screen. Their demeanour was unusual and demanded a respectful hush. I can't exactly say why, but my memories of the whole Foot and Mouth experience unfold in a similar way; slow, grey-dark and funereal.

A DISASTER UNFOLDS

We were in London on the day that Foot and Mouth Disease (FMD) was discovered; a rare family break at a friend's flat in the heart of the city and a million miles away from our usual rural backwater. After the debacle surrounding BSE, I remember thinking, 'Here we go, now it's the pigs' turn, but at least they'll have this one under control'. It never entered my head again—until we got home.

The discovery of the disease in pigs at the Cheale Meats abattoir in Essex on Tuesday 20th February 2001 was soon traced to a likely source for the outbreak. By Friday it was confirmed that Ronnie and Bobby Waugh's pig-fattening unit at Heddon-on-the-Wall in Northumberland had infected animals that may have been harbouring the disease for over a fortnight. (Pigs, if infected, spread the disease by breathing out a viral plume, and it can quickly spread to cattle and sheep.) Improperly processed catering swill was thought to be to blame. If true it was a disaster waiting to happen.

Way back in 1927 it was shown that the virus could survive in frozen meat for seventy-six days, and

Philip Lake bringing the cows in for milking,
Ramscliffe Farm, Beaford, North Devon

in chilled meat indefinitely. Whilst the Foods Standards Agency advises that FMD cannot be transmitted to humans within the food chain, an avenue exists for the virus to pass to animals. Uncooked waste containing bones, offal and lymph glands of dead animals, such as lamb, cattle and pigs, is a perfect reservoir for the disease. To satisfy consumer demand we import a large amount of meat, mostly from the EU, but also from countries where FMD is endemic, and where attention to animal welfare is less rigorous than our own. Although this meat is routinely imported deboned from animals vaccinated against FMD, it is possible that a contaminated shipment had slipped through the net. Another route for the virus could have been through the import of *illegal* meat. According to official estimates, only 2% of illegal imports are seized at the point of entry. A finger was also pointed at the nearby Albemarle Barracks from where, it was suggested, the Waughs had obtained swill. Under EU procurement rules, the armed forces must buy their meat from the cheapest source. Albemarle's regiment may have been marching on their stomachs, but not necessarily on British procured meat.

But just how the disease had come to be at Burnside Farm was already being buried. The Ministry of Agriculture, Fisheries and Food (MAFF) dodged the issue when questioned about the source, saying that it might not have been swill or, if it was, it could have come from schools, hotels or local Chinese restaurants. (The Chinese community, quite naturally, went spare.)

But, on the point of animal welfare, we are not exactly whiter than white either. Pigs travelling from Northumberland to Essex in order to be slaughtered are symptomatic of the way livestock movements have increased in the last few decades. It is true that we have always moved stock, and sometimes long distances. The country is criss-crossed with old drovers' roads and with the coming of the railways livestock could be moved more easily. Britain was famous for its breeding stock and it was in great demand from abroad. But animals as a commodity, to be traded like fruit and vegetables, along with the disappearance of the smaller, local abattoirs have led to large numbers of live animals embarking on ridiculously long, arduous journeys. It may be the way the market dictates, but there is clearly little room for compassion within the system.

Longtown Market in Carlisle, Cumbria is one of the biggest sheep markets in Europe. It had become a magnet for dealers and their agents who would then sell on to the meat processing companies. It was not unusual for as many as 14,000 sheep to be sold in one day.

Sheep from a farm close to the pig unit at Heddon-on-the-Wall had already been through Longtown Market and sold. On 15th February the gavel fell on a pen of just nine Texel cull ewes, bought by the livestock dealer Willie Cleave from Devon. He'd been in the business for twenty-five years and clearly had no idea of the ravages he was about to cause. There were, at this point, no visible signs of disease. The next day the same sheep were on his farm at Highampton in Devon, infecting other sheep and cattle, which in the normal course of his business were to be sold to other parts of the country and also abroad. Then, on the weekend of the 24th February, Willie Cleave realised that something was horribly wrong. The animals on his

home farm were showing the tell-tale symptoms of Foot and Mouth.

When the disease was confirmed on the following day the news struck the Westcountry like a thunderbolt. We were the biggest livestock area in the country. There wasn't time to question the policy of how to handle the disease. They had immediately slaughtered in the last outbreak in 1967, and it seemed they would do so again. Some 600 cattle and 1500 sheep, along with a herd of goats, were earmarked for slaughter and incineration on Willie Cleave's farms. The television pictures of pyres being lit in Northumberland, remote as yet, were to become a familiar and painful scene on our doorstep.

A ban was already in place on all susceptible livestock movements and, as each day brought new cases, the countryside was forced to shut down. On the 27th February the whole of Dartmoor was declared an infected area due to the discovery of the disease on two farms between Okehampton and Holsworthy. Although these farms were some distance from the moor, the traditional grazing in open country was perceived as a potential springboard for the disease.

Once the closure of all footpaths and bridleways was in place (28th February) we began to feel like prisoners in our own homes. The familiar sounds, sights and smells had changed and an oppressive atmosphere was beginning to blight our lives. I relate the following story as I remember it, told to me in what seemed an unlikely place at the time.

I had gone into Exeter with my youngest son who was not yet five years old. He had amused me by suggesting that we roam the moors in the nude 'because the disease only sticks to your wellies and clothes'. His young mind was frustrated at not being able to visit his familiar haunts and footpaths.

After a swimming lesson in Crediton we had taken to going to the city museum in an attempt to bring about some form of normality to our lives. Although, in the circumstances, I found looking at stuffed animals a little incongruous, he thoroughly enjoyed learning about them and the smile on his face paid dividends.

We had left the museum and gone into Marks and Spencer's for lunch. Jed was clutching a small model of a dinosaur that I had bought in the museum shop, and I had asked him to find a table while I joined the queue to the till. When I rounded the corner I found him sat at a table in deep conversation with an elderly lady. She smiled and told me he had been educating her on the eating habits of different dinosaurs. 'He's very knowledgeable!'

The conversation inevitably got round to FMD. Then, in a quiet tone, she told me that she and her husband once had a farm near Looe in Cornwall....

'In 1952 we got Foot and Mouth in a small herd of bullocks. Although you were supposed to notify the Ministry, my husband didn't hold with what they might do. He kept them away from the house in a field next to the sea. They were tucked in under the hedge and had plenty of food and water. Within a fortnight they were over it and as far as he was concerned, none the worse for wear.'

I was stunned. Could this be true? It was hard to look at her and think 'how utterly irresponsible',

John Harding winter-feeding, Wonson Manor,
Throwleigh, Dartmoor

for it occurred to me that the bulletins put out each day by the National Farmers' Union (South West Region) often referred to farms that had animals under suspicion, which, after testing, proved to be clear. Perhaps her bullocks never had the disease—or could they have recovered? Just how accurate was this test? Vets were already beginning to argue and a growing number of people were criticising the policy of slaughtering 'so-called' dangerous contacts, demanding an alternative. There was talk of a homeopathic remedy, in the form of Borax 30 added to drinking water, which whilst not conferring immunity was claimed to reduce the susceptibility to infection. And what about vaccination? It was admitted that the disease was difficult to recognise in sheep and that in some infected flocks only five per cent of animals showed any outward signs. The disease may have been present in some sheep flocks for a lot longer than previously thought.

Seeking reliable information on the subject did not always give clear answers. The Ministry had never vaccinated in previous outbreaks although the Northumberland Report, published in 1969, acknowledged that there might be a role for ring vaccination to curb the spread. But vaccination would also lengthen the time it would take to re-gain our status as an FMD-free country. It was clear that the long-term financial implications would have considerable bearing on current policy making.

With so many different agendas the Government struggled to steer a clear line, especially as a general election was imminent. We began to see suggestions from intelligent, qualified people on how to handle the outbreak dismissed and rebuffed. It is not the first time that a government, finding itself in crisis, has revealed an ugly face and has adopted the arrogant stance of 'nanny knows best'.

On the 11th March the National Farmers' Union put out a sombre statement on their daily bulletin:

'It is now twenty days since the outbreak was first identified at Cheale Meats in Essex, and seventeen days since the nationwide movement of stock was stopped. Now that the fourteen-day quarantine period has passed, vets had hoped that new outbreaks would have dried up. With another twelve cases confirmed so far today, there

THE SHIPPING FORECAST

Each farm an island, cut off from the main,
Vortex of hedgerows, green seas, treacherous
Tangle of uncharted reefs, destiny unfathomed.

Flotsam and jetsam, man and beast, live cargo
Cast adrift, ride out the storm as best they can,
Hatches battened down in byre, barn, linhay and leaze.

Invisible currents swirl ever closer,
Rage beneath the surface, till the tidal wave,
At any moment. Mayday. Mayday.

A cataclysm glued to the radio. Instinct and salvage.
'There are warnings of severe gales in sea areas Plymouth,
Sole, Lundy, Fastnet, Irish Sea. General Synopsis at 0700.

Complex low developing along the A3072 between Holsworthy
And Hatherleigh 993 deepening rapidly 979 by 1300 tomorrow.
Area forecasts for the next 24 hours: North Devon

South West Gale 10 occasionally gusting 12
Heavy showers. Visibility five furlongs. Outlook poor.'
Mayday. Mayday. Yet it is only the Ides of March.

is obviously no sign of this happening. There is fortunately little evidence of wind-borne spread, or of transmission on vehicles (although there are a number of cases where the source is still unknown). Instead, it seems that sheep, moved before the movement ban, have introduced the disease to areas where it lies undetected until it transfers to cattle or erupts in stressed sheep. There could therefore be outbreaks of the disease in new areas for some time to come.'

A few days later the Government announced a new, proactive slaughter campaign.

In Devon all farms within a three-kilometre radius of a confirmed outbreak were to be inspected every two days by a MAFF vet. At the first sign of any symptoms, the animals would be slaughtered.

In addition to this, all the sheep that had been handled by two key individuals since the start of the outbreak would be traced and slaughtered. The individuals weren't actually named, but one was certainly Willie Cleave, the Devon based dealer. All sheep moved through the markets of Longtown on the 15th February, Welshpool on the 19th and Northampton on the 22nd would also be traced, and these animals, plus all the animals that had come into contact with them, would be slaughtered.

But for the north of the country the policy had a different slant:

In Cumbria and South Scotland all animals within a three-kilometre ring of an infected farm were to be slaughtered and the Army called in to help with their management and disposal.

On a weekend in early March I received a telephone call to say there was a suspected outbreak on Dartmoor, somewhere in the centre of the moor. The caller wasn't sure where. I called other friends and finally got an answer. The problem was at Dunnabridge Farm, right in the heart of the moor. How on earth had it got there? **DEATH ABOVE THE DART** The farm was at least 20 miles south of the outbreak at Willie Cleave's. If this was infection travelling on the wind then no farm was safe. The outbreak was confirmed the next day.

There was a fall of snow that weekend and one thing that struck me was just how many animal tracks were criss-crossing the fields around our house. They weren't the footprints of stock but those of wild animals. I had already noted the crows and rooks becoming so much bolder since the ban on using footpaths was put in place. When I went out to feed the chickens in the morning, squadrons of black menacing birds would take off from the distant trees, weaving their way directly to our house. The skies looked like a scene from the Battle of Britain. They became so persistent that I gave up trying to beat them off, at-tempting instead to creep out to the pen without being heard. And it was plain for all to see. No matter what restrictions you put in place to limit farm animal movements, there was no way that you could stop the deer, foxes, badgers or birds from migrating to and fro.

It's a strange thing, but a crisis, whether personal or national, creates time for reflection. One morning, after feeding the chickens, I walked on to the top lawn and stared up at the leaden sky. A stiff wind was crackling through the beech trees and the damned birds were there again, wheeling endlessly above our rooftop. Their squawking cries seemed to mock my very presence, for they were certainly annoyed with me, and a rather sobering thought crossed my mind. Had this been a human disease, an unstoppable plague, this is how life in the countryside might emerge. Nature, unfettered and wild, back in a world without us.

By now the crisis was having a serious effect on my business. As a documentary photographer commissions tend to come in fits and starts and you find yourself being a jack-of-all-trades in order to survive.

Michael Mudge at lambing time, Huccaby Farm,
Dartmoor

A small part of my income came from guided walks on the moor. I kissed goodbye to that. I did have one lucrative commission lined up to document an auction on a West Devon farm. The new owners had approached the outgoing farmers and asked if they would mind me being there with my camera. It had all been approved but suddenly the sale was cancelled because of MAFF's restrictions on movement. I wasn't worried as such for after 26 years as a freelance I had learnt how to survive—there's a little of Dickens' Mr Micawber in me in that I always believe something will turn up.

And so it did. I can't remember the exact date but one morning I received a heartening phone call from Devon County Council about a photographic commission they had initiated through Beaford Arts in North Devon.

'We've been discussing the crisis and wondered if you would be interested? We cannot grant you any special privileges or give you access to restricted areas but this crisis is devastating for Devon and we think you would be a good person to make a set of pictures—a sort of historical record?'

Rising to the challenge and flattered by their faith in me I immediately accepted, but I remember thinking then how on earth would I go about it?

I had already been keeping a watchful eye on developments up on the moor. Four days had passed since the discovery of the disease at Dunnabridge. Michael and Rosemary Mudge at Huccaby Farm had land that fell within the three-kilometre radius. Rosemary told me in a tearful voice on the telephone how they couldn't get a straight answer from MAFF.

'They've found nothing on our farm and one minute they say they won't slaughter, the next they say they might. The waiting is sheer hell. Anton (Coaker) at Sherberton is for holding out against them.'

I felt rather useless, truly wanting to help. These people were well known to me. I had photographed their daughter Lindsay's wedding the previous year, a lovely occasion where, as a bride, she had walked with her father and mother from the farmhouse down the road to the chapel and then back up the hill with her new husband for a reception in the barn. It was a country wedding full of laughter and joy. Now they were suffering a nightmare no one could ever have envisaged.

Then on the 17th March Lindsay, knowing I was an ally in their plight, rang to tell me that the slaughter had begun and a pyre was being built in the meadow against the Dartmeet road at the top of the lane, 'one of Dad's favourite fields'. She said that they wouldn't close the road until they were ready to light the pyre, it being the main artery from Ashburton across the moor, but if I wanted pictures I would have to stay off the farm.

The family had been through absolute hell. Although the Winsors at Dunnabridge Farm had phoned them on Saturday 3rd March to say that they were certain that their stock had Foot and Mouth, it wasn't until midday Monday that MAFF informed the Mudges. That afternoon an official turned up to serve a Form D notice on the farm, asking for details of farm boundaries and the whereabouts of stock. (Form D was served on premises where there was a suspected outbreak, or on premises where the animals were regarded as 'dangerous contacts'). The next day a MAFF vet, together with an assistant, arrived to check the animals. But it came as no surprise to the family that their stock was found to be free from disease. They knew their animals.

But their sighs of relief weren't to last long. When the Mudges sat down to watch the local news that night they stared at the screen in disbelief. During an item highlighting the plight at Dunnabridge, it was announced that all of the Mudges' stock would be slaughtered. Later an embarrassed MAFF vet, John Hanwell, rang the family to apologise:

'It should not have gone out. I'm really sorry. No decision has been taken. Your stock have a fifty-fifty chance of repeal.'

Wednesday morning and another telephone call from someone at the MAFF headquarters in Exeter asking yet again for a tally of the farm's livestock and details of the land boundaries. Their apparent muddle hardly inspired confidence. When pressed about the future of their animals, the official replied that a decision would be made within twenty-four hours. On the farm all the stock remained healthy.

At 4.55pm on Thursday the Mudges received the phone call they had been dreading. All the stock

Lindsay Mudge on her wedding day, Huccaby Farm,
Dartmoor

would be valued and then killed, 'hopefully the next day'. But after a number of phone calls it was found that the valuers were too busy. Saturday was the earliest they could come,

Whilst this would normally have compounded the agony, for the family it bought a little time. On Friday morning, with their animals still fit and healthy, the Mudges made a number of desperate calls to their local MP's, the National Park Authority, the National Farmers' Union and most revealing, to the epidemiologist who had made the decision to cull.

Lindsay pleaded with him. 'Why is it that neighbouring farms on either side of us who only have housed cattle will not be culled? None of our land butts against Dunnabridge and the land in-between is empty of livestock. The MAFF vet has seen our livestock regularly—they are to date healthy livestock. And why is Tor Royal having its newtake culled but not its housed livestock, even though the same farmer feeds both sets of animals?'

His answer was firm though somewhat flawed. The livestock in all of these sheds was outside the three-kilometre zone, and so the risk of infection was less. Frustrated, she began to tell everyone she could think of the history of the Huccaby herd. Dad had built the stock up from just four cows. They were extremely robust and healthy and had an inbuilt immunity against Red Water (a sometimes fatal disease caused by exposure to ticks and common in newly grazed livestock on Dartmoor). But the more people Lindsay rang, the more hopeless it seemed. The Chief Executive of the Dartmoor National Park Authority, Nick Atkinson, said he could not get involved. Anthony Gibson, the Regional Director of the National Farmers' Union (the Mudges had been fully paid up members for years) gave a promise that he would 'get back to her'. The MP's said they would take it forward, but made little progress. The phone remained silent.

Then on Saturday morning, whilst feeding the stock, the Mudges caught site of the pyre now burning at Dunnabridge. A telephone call to Michael Mudge from Prince Charles momentarily boosted morale. (Huccaby Farm, like Dunnabridge, is a Duchy of Cornwall tenancy.) But later in the morning John Hanwell rang again. He said that he wanted to arrange for a valuer to come and view the stock.

Rosemary asked him what would happen then? 'They will be slaughtered.'

Not to be outdone, she asked him a probing question:

'What has happened to the Winsors' 'so-called' infected stock that are at Two Bridges?' (These were on land on the opposite side of Dunnabridge and further up river).

He replied:

'We are monitoring them.'

Rosemary fired back at him:

'Then why not monitor ours! I want to speak to someone in higher authority. I cannot allow valuers onto our farm knowing that the 'so-called' infected stock belonging to the Winsors are still alive!'

A secretary rang and asked if she could make an appointment for the valuation, but if MAFF thought that the female touch was going to soften Rosemary, they were very much mistaken. Once again she said no, not until she had spoken to someone in higher authority.

Finally Ben Bennett, a senior MAFF vet, telephoned to say that the epidemiologist had maintained that everything within the three-kilometre ring had to be culled. 'There can be no appeal.' (Compare this statement with the guidelines announced by Prime Minister Tony Blair at a conference in Exeter two weeks later: 'in Devon, holdings which adjoin farms on which there have been confirmed outbreaks of FMD will not automatically have their susceptible livestock slaughtered. Instead, the vets have been given discretion to adapt the policy to local conditions'.)

Ignoring what Bennett was saying, Rosemary pleaded further. 'Why not use our stock as a buffer zone? We feed all our stock daily and we are calving and lambing. Everything is checked and counted daily. We all know what to look for in Foot and Mouth and all the stock is ring fenced and cannot roam.' But her cries fell on deaf ears. One insensitive MAFF official even had the audacity to ask the question: 'OK, so we let your animals live. How will you feel if FMD then spreads to the rest of Dartmoor?'

Sunday and Monday came and went. Then on Tuesday the vet and the valuers arrived. 'At the end of the afternoon we were given 10 pieces of paper, 10 pieces of paper that catalogued Mum and Dad's blood, sweat and tears of the last 37 years. It was a dreadful day.' The next morning Lindsay's brother David went up to Sherberton Farm to help Anton Coaker with the slaughter of his animals. They too were fit and healthy.

On Friday 16th March, 13 days after the outbreak at Dunnabridge and contrary to government policy, the slaughter of the Mudges' fit and healthy animals began. (The contiguous cull policy came into force at a later date and only applied to Cumbria and South Scotland. In Devon, all animals within a three-kilometre ring of an outbreak were supposed to be tested every two days.)

It was with some trepidation that I set off for Huccaby Farm that afternoon, and when I arrived the spectacle was worse than imagined. This was the field where, two years before, I had photographed Michael Mudge tending his sheep at lambing time, always a positive time in the farming calendar. Now it was churned into mud and soil, with rows of carcasses piled high on beds of sleepers, straw bales and coal. Busy tractors and trailers, filled beyond the brim with dead cattle, were arriving one after another whilst on the ground men in white overalls, hooded and impossible to identify, stood directing operations. I climbed on to the bank behind the granite wall and attached a long telephoto lens to my camera. Suddenly I spotted Michael driving one of the tractors. I waved awkwardly. I think he recognised me, but his eyes were wide and his face numb, fixed in an expression of dazed control and utter disbelief at what he was doing.

I took a few pictures, spotting the carcass of a fine South Devon Bull, then realised I wasn't alone. Another photographer, also sporting a long telephoto lens, this time on a digital camera, had climbed the verge. I turned and asked if he was local. 'No, I work for the *Telegraph*. I was down covering another story when I was told about this.' He fired a few shots then showed me the images on the back of his camera, explaining that he would wire them to the London office immediately via a laptop in his car. He didn't seem at all fazed at what he was photographing, and after about ten minutes he left.

Once he'd gone I started to feel uneasy. This wasn't the way that I worked. I was no press photographer; I'd never had the stomach for it. It's not that I despised the profession (one or two of my former students had made successful careers in the industry) it was just that I had always chosen to work slowly and steadily. It didn't matter to me if a story took weeks to develop. But working for a newspaper demands working to a deadline and there is considerable pressure to come up with the goods. Photographs get taken in a flash and tomorrow you may be covering a totally different story. Occasionally there is a great picture which is worthy of an award, but most of it is simply daily fodder and is soon forgotten.

I had no confidence in the pictures I was taking. I knew there would be hundreds like them and I went home feeling terribly depressed.

But a few nights later I lay in bed and made a decision. I wouldn't desert the moor, but I was going to tackle this story in a different way. The commission from Beaford Arts had given me a lift. North Devon was a hotbed demanding attention. It was here that I would search for my story.

KEEP THE HOME FIRES BURNING

Aardvarks on the loose, handling the tail back.
Not since the Blitz has so much acrid smoke
Filled the air, clutched at lungs and livers,
The pyre upon which wool does not yet burn.

Legs outstretched for valuation,
Hide and seek. Rigor mortis, bloated stench.
Unremitting the politics of disease,
Veterinary science at its most baffling.

Small farms that have struggled
Through a thousand winters
Now endure the cameras, a bleak future.
No calling of cattle in the early morning,

Only the sweet smell of hay well made
Left lingering in the long barn.
In a twinkling the heart torn out of the moor.
The Hound of the Baskervilles is out tonight.

Hoisting cattle onto the funeral pyre,
Huccaby Farm, Dartmoor

Bringing carcasses to the funeral pyre,
Huccaby Farm, Dartmoor

PYRE

Today we have burning of pyres.
Yesterday it was slaughtering of animals
And the day before that
We had movement of animals.

The gentle swell and burst of gastric juices
Effervescing in the bright sunlight,
A putrid muzzle stretched
Over your face, drowning the smell.

A dull sheen doused with diesel,
Smoke screen half a mile wide
Soaring to the heavens,
A ghostly suffocating pallor

Within which white figures move.
In slow motion, anonymous hooded vultures
Prod the fire, tickle the beast,
Flames that lick the countryside into shape.

Today we have burning of pyres.
And tomorrow we will have digging of pits
And then the filling in of pits. And after that
A slow dull silence that eats away at the concrete.

FOOT AND MOUTH

There is fear in the air.
You can feel it climbing over hedges
Passing from farm to farm
Invisibly trailing its white coat
Across the fields.

You can hear it crackle
Like a forest fire.
It lives in kitchens
And in the news reports,
In the eyes of children
And in the hunched expressions
Of their animals.

Even the dogs have gone wild
With uncertainty.

Farm entrance, Beaford, North Devon

Produce sign, Ramscliffe Farm, Beaford,
North Devon

With my attention now turned on North Devon, I rang Beaford Arts for some help. I spoke to the then director, Jennie Hayes, and asked if she could come up with a list of people who would be willing to talk to me. There was nothing formed in my mind as yet but at least it would be a start. She promptly came back with a list of farmers she believed would make good contacts, together with their telephone numbers. One by one I worked my way down the list, but the response was always the same. 'We'd love to talk to you, but we are terrified of getting this disease and are sealed in. Maybe phone us again in a fortnight.' I then dialled the number for Ramscliffe.

Five months later I wrote the following account for my archive. It's as fresh in my mind today as it was then, and I don't believe I shall ever forget it.

* * *

When Nigel Lake, at Brealeys Farm, Beaford, telephoned his uncle on the evening of the 18th March to tell him that the cows had Foot and Mouth, the news brought shock and despair. The downturn in farming, coupled with the filthy wet weather, had already caused misery and for the past few weeks all talk had centred on the imminent threat of disease. The parish lies to the east of the River Torridge in North Devon, and every farm had been waiting in fear.

SILENCE AT RAMSCLIFFE

By now all confidence in the Government's ability to control the outbreak was lost. Whatever trust people had placed in the Ministry of Agriculture, Fisheries and Food was in tatters, and rumour and counter rumour were rife. Across the North Devon countryside the pyres were being lit and the air was filled with a reek and heavy atmosphere as if we were at war. Indeed, every day my neighbour on Dartmoor, who keeps a small flock of pedigree sheep, would relate yet another hushed story that he had heard on the now confused and deeply suspicious grapevine: 'A phial of virus has gone missing from MAFF's laboratory at Pirbright. A golden handkerchief is available at a price and some farmers are deliberately infecting their stock. So and so has moved his sheep without a license in the middle of the night; he couldn't bear it, the foxes were eating his lambs. A dealer lending sheep caused

Percy Lake out on the milk round, Beaford,
North Devon

Philip Lake milking his cows, Ramscliffe Farm,
Beaford, North Devon

that outbreak up on the moor. They reckon they were boosting the numbers to claim the subsidy.'

And the strain on my neighbour's face was beginning to show. Gone was his gentle and friendly sparkle, replaced by a shroud of unbelievable tiredness and worry. One morning he leaned out of his Land Rover window at a group of us on the lane. 'Those dogs should be on a lead,' he grumbled, and then immediately drove off as if regretting the outburst. We murmured amongst ourselves, arguing his point but nevertheless sympathetic to the cause.

My first day at Ramscliffe Farm that April was a pleasant one, for after weeks of interminable rain the sun suddenly shone. When I got to the farmhouse Philip Lake and his father Percy were in good spirits. I had telephoned a few days before, explaining my wish to make a series of pictures about the crisis, and Philip said he was keen to meet me. He told me that his cousin's farm in Beaford, which neighboured his land, had gone down with the disease. They had already gone through a period of immense shock and were now resigned to the likelihood of being either the next to catch it or

taken out on the contiguous cull. 'You come down boy, it'll be good to see you.'

Farming is a responsible occupation for there are animals involved, and they need you as much as you need them. For most farmers their welfare is paramount and no matter how bad the weather, how small the profit, there is a duty, coupled with pride, to see them right. Father and son showed me over the farm as they went about their business. Philip fetched a large round bale of straw on the fore-end loader whilst Percy fed the calves. Then together they worked through the yards, laying the straw down for bedding in the various sheds and cubicles. By late afternoon it was time to milk again. Percy went home, semi-retired now in a bungalow in the village, whilst Philip brought in the cows. As he milked for the second time that day I watched the proceedings and marvelled at the calm. Cows in milk are a picture of contentment.

I arranged my next visit for Friday. In between the visits a valuation was made of all the stock on the farm. It was now only a matter of time and, although official observation recorded no disease,

Philip Lake talking to his bank manager on the
morning of the cull, Ramscliffe Farm, Beaford,
North Devon

THE LAND

The land has lost its marbles,
Limb by limb, flock by flock
Tearing itself apart.

Consigned to record books,
Pedigree herds homogenised,
Computerised, evaporated.

Bottled up, the phoney war.
Virtual litres wiped off the screen,
Milk yields stuck on some hard disk.

Incinerated in an instant,
Generations down the tube.
Delete, delete, delete.

Philip Lake emptying the slurry tank,
Ramscliffe Farm, Beaford, North Devon

the outcome was inevitable. Percy and his wife Roma had volunteered to do the milk round to take the strain off Philip and I agreed to join them at 7.30 am. It was a cold grey morning but as yet dry. I raced around Beaford on foot as Roma read out the orders and Percy dropped off the plastic bottles on each doorstep, occasionally getting it wrong and suffering a reprimand from the delivery jeep! Soon it was nine o'clock and, satisfied with my pictures, I drove down to the farm. Philip had finished his morning's milking and had just received a phone call from MAFF. 'It's happening today. They're coming at eleven o'clock to cull the animals.'

Philip had spent the night away. Divorced for some time, he had got back into the swing of the bachelor life but never shunned his duty to his cows. He was visibly tired and smoking incessantly, but was also calling on some inner strength, braced and ready. He asked me to stay, suggesting that MAFF would think I was his farmhand who happened to be away on holiday. I laughed at the suggestion. I was wearing a brand new pair of overalls, which I had bought for the assignment, putting them through the recommended hot wash each night when I arrived home. A pair of wellingtons and a flat cap may have completed the picture but my attire looked far too new and not altogether convincing! Impersonation was not a comfortable option. I said that I would play it by ear.

The telephone rang, piercing the uncomfortable quiet. It was his bank manager. 'No, no, I'm fine Janet. Quite honestly it's a relief. It's impossible to farm at the moment what with this weather and all the restrictions.' They chatted away whilst I made more coffee.

Finishing his second cup Philip suddenly sprang into action. 'I've got to empty that slurry tank before they come else they'll have me.' I assured him it would be the last thing on their minds. Ignoring me, he started the tractor and fetched the spreader and in no time at all had sucked out the tank and sprayed the liquid onto the field in front of the farmhouse. Happy to be working he then set about cleaning the yard of the gallons of urine and muck that had accumulated over the last few days. Restrictions had meant that the stock were hanging around the

Philip Lake spreading slurry on the morning of
the cull, Ramscliffe Farm, Beaford, North Devon

immediate environs of the farm and that, coupled with a high water table, was causing misery for both farmer and beast. Ramscliffe was drowning in slurry.

The slaughterman was the first to arrive, a tall, bald-headed man from Launceston in Cornwall. He was well versed in soothing away a farmer's fears and anxiety and soon put Philip at ease. (He was less sure of me, however, spotting my camera lying on the kitchen table.) We chewed the fat and he told us how he played the stock market, and how it wasn't too clever at the moment. He had volunteered for this, he said, as it was good money. Soon the rest of the team arrived headed by a vet from a practice in East Devon. There was an AI man, who lived in Essex, and a young man who had just finished a training course somewhere up-country with MAFF. ('It's my first day on this,' he explained to me later.)

We all shook hands and I immediately asked the vet for a word in private. I didn't want to embarrass him (or myself) in front of the others. Inside the kitchen I came clean, explaining that I wasn't Philip's farmhand, but a photographer here to make a record for the Beaford Archive. I showed him my cameras and a file of paperwork, in it a letter confirming my commission. He was surprised and drew breath. It was clear that I had presented him with a dilemma. 'Look,' I said, 'you have two options. You can tell me to clear off and I will go home right now, or you can let me stay and I will chip in and help. But this needs documenting. We've seen enough of burning pyres. I'm not from the newspapers and I don't have an angle. I'm simply here to record a piece of history.'

There was a pause and then without looking up he snapped at me. 'OK, you can stay, but I want you in white overalls and that camera wrapped in a plastic bag.' I felt a flush of relief followed by an awkward feeling of joy. Being honest had paid off.

In need of the regulation overalls the vet suddenly realised he had forgotten to seal off the lane so he raced me up the hill to his car. I tried to strike up a conversation about the merits of the contiguous cull but his brow furrowed. 'You have to look at the bigger picture' was all he could offer. He was in

Philip Lake cleaning the yard, Ramscliffe Farm,
Beaford, North Devon

DANGER—NOTIFIABLE DISEASE

In silence, the overall situation.
Hung, drawn and quartered,
Entrails burnt in Studio 4
Sentences handed down to condemned prisoners.

No leniency for good behaviour. No parole.
No quarantine for the healthy.
The video nasty arrives on the doorstep.
Judge Jeffreys hard at it in the killing sheds,

'Don't waste ye court's time by pleading ye innocence'
'Massacre of the Unsuspecting', Fast forward
'Quirks of the Spanish Inquisition', re-run, again and again.
Ritual slaughter coming to a farm near you.

Primitive pits overlain with old railway sleepers,
Straw, pallets, kerosene, red diesel and coal,
Ready to burn, witches at the stake,
Scapegoats etched into the impatient skyline.

The virulent disease, elusive, hounded, snookered,
A new strain bulldozed into a corner.
The smell of death crumbling in on itself,
Rook to Queen's pawn. Pot black. Pol Pot. Check mate.

Robert Kilby sealing the lane to the farm,
Ramscliffe, Beaford, North Devon

Philip Lake taking bedding down to the silage clamp
prior to the slaughter, Ramscliffe Farm, Beaford

Spreading straw in the silage clamp prior to the
slaughter, Ramscliffe Farm, Beaford

FAREWELL TO AGRICULTURE?

Each day another herd is rounded up,
Another rendezvous at some disputed barricade.
Farm gates galvanised and padlocked,
Narrow lanes cowed into submission.

D notices issued like confetti, D for disinfectant.
D for Destruction, Decay, Decimate, Defecate.
Unable to move, animals are held
For questioning as virtual deadlines run out.

Shot like hostages one by one
Obscure sheds thick with blood and urine.
The civil war creeping forward,
Armageddon on your doorstep.

Vietnam in North Devon and Cumbria,
Hedgerows rank with inquisitive film crews
Relaying the drama as if it was Beirut,
Jerusalem, the West Bank.

In England's green and pleasant land,
Digital images broadcast every night
Into the sofa-safe soft plush depths
Of countless suburban sitting rooms.

Contorted carcasses slung upside down
Between the adverts, outstretched digger arms.
Long lines of flickering flames,
Night's curfew: anguish on a farmer's face.

Philip Lake herding the store cattle down to the yard
for sedation, Ramscliffe Farm, Beaford

work mode now and the job in hand required all his concentration. I donned the overalls, photographed him sealing the track with the official blue and white tape and then marched back down to the farm in silence. Threatening skies were producing the first few spots of rain.

Philip was in the yard with the others helping to tie together a system of gates. He whispered to me that he would help move the cattle but he didn't want to watch anything being killed. The heavens opened and the recently cleaned yard shone like an olive green mirror as a thin layer of residue muck diluted and spread. The milking cows were brought in first, confused at the strange break in routine. They assembled in the yard in front of the milking parlour and were then coaxed inside and into the stalls with a little food. One by one each cow was sedated, released and gently ushered out and along to the covered silage clamp, empty now of last year's harvest. Philip brought clean straw in a vain attempt to give them something to lie on, but the now heavy rain swelled the already over-brimming farm springs and pools of water gathered on the concrete floor.

As the clamp filled with sedated cows I was shocked to see one cow walk over to another lying motionless on the floor. She sniffed for recognition, staring at the body as if in disbelief. It was chillingly human. Another came in and did exactly the same and they both stood there rooted to the spot. It may have been the effect of the sedative, but it occurred to me that we so easily dismiss the notion that animals too have feelings.

When all the cows were sedated the slaughter began. One by one the captive bolt gun was raised to each head and the trigger released. There was a dull crack with a rush of visible gas from the steel barrel and the cow slumped to the floor. There then followed a few moments of twitching as she expelled her dying breath.

The vet and the AI man followed on behind, inserting a blue rod into the hole made by the gun into the brain, and pushing down into the spinal cord. A vigorous stir and it was all over. Clambering over a growing sea of bodies, each animal death was confirmed and its carcass marked with a blue dye, sprayed from an aerosol.

As the day dragged on it was the turn of the in-calf heifers. Again Philip helped round them up and drove them into the cattle crush to be sedated, but as they were being killed he disappeared indoors. By late afternoon there were rumbles of needing a break and I volunteered to make everyone a cup of tea. The weather improved and there was talk of light at the end of the tunnel. Philip sneaked off into the village for some tobacco and asked me to cover for him. When he came back, unnoticed, they started on the calves. Philip darted back indoors. I watched as they were led across the yard, the last one having to be carried. I had seen enough. I couldn't photograph them being shot. I wandered about the farm in a daze.

I have often wondered why so many war photographs are technically poor. The images either suffer from too much contrast or are badly focussed with the end result appearing cold and raw. But now I can see that using a camera in such circumstances is not an easy task. I am used to photographing everyday life, its ups as well as downs, but the events of this particular day were surreal.

I kept pressing the shutter as if in a dream, my senses bludgeoned and in shock.

Since then, as the months have passed, I've been able to look at the pictures in a different light. The story needed telling from a human perspective and despite the horror I am now strangely pleased with the result. The rights and wrongs of the contiguous cull are yet to be debated, but there is no doubt that the Foot and Mouth crisis has highlighted all that is going wrong in farming. It seems, often through no fault of their own, that farmers are pushing too hard, tied into a system that demands that they produce more to survive.

But for me the day is remembered as one of unbelievable waste, a sickening solution to what many believe was an unnecessary crisis in the countryside. And because of it Ramscliffe, a small, good, typical North Devon dairy farm, has, for now, joined the ranks of the silent.

Chris Chapman, September 2001
Throwleigh
Devon

PLEASE KEEP OUT

Make way for the Ministry of Slaughter.
Each blister is under investigation,
Each small lesion, hoof, lip and tongue
Inspected, the slightest frothing at the mouth.

Early symptoms: dehydration,
Rapid loss of condition, lameness,
Eyes that do not respond. Trial by laboratory.
Antibodies. Personal vetting on a vast scale.

Then the awful truth confirmed by MAFF.
The shoot to kill policy. Summary executions,
As if Goya was on hand as a marksman,
Or Hieronymus Bosch employed as a war artist.

The captive bolt, the virus of disbelief
Trapped behind barbed wire and bureaucracy
You've seen long lines of assassinations
Dangerous contacts, guilty by association.

S.O.S. Slaughter on Suspicion.
Stalin's purges coming home to roost,
Animal Farm and Guernica.
Passchendaele revisited a thousand times.

Each small lesion, hoof, lip and tongue
Inspected, the slightest frothing.
Rapid loss of condition.
Lameness. Eyes that do not respond.

MAFF employee herding cattle,
Ramscliffe Farm, Beaford

Sedating the store cattle before their slaughter,
Ramscliffe Farm, Beaford

The sedated dairy herd awaiting slaughter,
Ramscliffe Farm, Beaford

THE LAST STRAW

Bedding down
Creature comforts
The Last Rites

The sky reflected
As if nothing was wrong
An act of kindness

Betrayal
Lives that have not yet
Had their full span

Thrown into the wind
An empty space
Where the heart should be

MAFF employee monitoring the sedation of the
dairy herd, Ramscliffe Farm, Beaford

A MILITARY OPERATION

At three removes, you've seen the flames
Flickering across impatient screens.
Names of remote farms and villages

Now familiar, as if it was Kosovo, Bosnia
Or Northern Ireland taming the darkness,
The funeral pyre fit for a dozen chieftains

A cleansing operation, as trigger happy
Slaughtermen take out the cloven hoof.
Mopping up behind enemy lines.

Fifth Column on the move,
Armed with clipboards and red berets
The logistics of body disposal,

Landfill, bone meal, gastric juices
Bloated beyond belief, exploding stomachs,
Festering sores, regimental orders.

The mechanics of graveyard humour
Eyeball to swollen eyeball,
Gallows birds that gather information

And spread the news to all and sundry.
'Still and still moving',
Tongue and oxtail, lambs for the chop.

Stunning a dairy cow with a captive bolt,
Ramscliffe Farm, Beaford

Tea break. Mid-afternoon on the day of the cull,
Ramscliffe Farm, Beaford

THE PASSWORD IS NO WORD AT ALL

At last Kafka has arrived in the countryside
Quivering in the night. Arrest that virus,
Illegal immigrant, detained for questioning.
The Outsider who does not belong.

The trial, abattoirs instead of abbots,
A new religious order in the making
Anointed with white overalls and hoods
Masks, a pale expression, the crime unspecified.

The reformatory, a refectory table
Arranged on the skyline
The last supper, sheep nuts and cattle cake
Crucified with ablutions and prayers.

Jehovah, the Old Testament Commissar,
Has returned, to visit his chosen people,
Fire and brimstone the only cure,
Cattle blood congealed upon the concrete floor.

Court orders carried out to the letter
In secret session. No chance of appeal, no redress.
In his saddle William Cobbett would have ranted
In his cottage John Clare would have wept.

Robert Kilby preparing the sedative for the calves,
Ramscliffe Farm, Beaford

The calf shed, Ramscliffe Farm, Beaford,
North Devon

THE DILEMMA

How do I tell a new born calf
That it is about to be shot and burned?

How do I look my neighbour in the eye
When I smell the rotten carcasses?

Where do I go when I see the smoke
Drifting across my land?

How do I tell the children
That they cannot go to school?

How do I look in the mirror in the morning?
What is it I see?

Why the lack of sleep?
Why the shotgun locked away?

Sedating the calves—Philip slips indoors,
Ramscliffe Farm, Beaford

Moving the calves to slaughter, Ramscliffe Farm,
Beaford

ANIMAL FARM

With each strand, each farm
A link with the land, severed,
The artery cut,

Littering the fields and yards.
Seen from the air
Another string of carcasses laid out

As if they were plastic imitations,
Toys scattered by a young child
Casually knocked over before supper.

Old MacDonald had a farm
Ee-i-ee-i-o
And on that farm he had some vets
Ee-i-ee-i-o

And the vets were looking here
And the vets were looking there
Looking here, looking there, looking everywhere

Old Macdonald had a farm
Ee-i-ee-i-o

Moving the last calf to slaughter,
Ramscliffe Farm, Beaford

71

THE KILL

First they inject, and for dairy herds
It is as they go out after the last milking.
A shot of sedative in the rump,
A gradual weariness that takes them by surprise.

Then the slaughterman dressed in white
Overalls to kill for, in his hands the captive bolt
The humane killer which punches a hole
Neatly through the skull, the front lobe

Just where you would use a pole-axe.
The dull sound of the compressed air cartridge
Echoes out across the yard. Time and time again
Animals slump, lie helpless in a heap.

Always it is the legs that go first, haphazardly,
The puppeteer quietly cuts the strings one by one.
Black and white, zebra pod of stranded whales,
Beached, they quiver, twitch, last breath expelled.

As if in trance, men wade through silence,
Waist deep, clamber over still warm bodies,
Riddle brains with the pither rod.
Skullduggery. Last rites, lad with a spray can.

Pithing and spraying the carcasses with dye,
Ramscliffe Farm, Beaford

Slaughtered dairy cows, Ramscliffe Farm, Beaford,
North Devon

IN LIMBO

Head to tail, on the hoof
Unblinking, door-stepped
Their last milking over
The texture of the skin
Ruckled on the neck
Like the surface of water
Ripples of sand
After the tide has gone out
Intimations of green fields,
Hedgerows
Hovering above the eyelid.

Calves, killing time.

THE CARCASSES KEEP COMING

Dead and stunned, silence gnaws
At the very soul of the countryside.
Unnerved and hovering in the wings
Sleek raven on patrol.

Lambs led to slaughter
Catapulted into the abyss,
An anthem for doomed livestock
Ear tagged and registered.

Scapegoats valued and valued again.
The accountant's nightmare,
The end of the road,
Four wheel drive and shotgun.

'What passing-bells for these who die as cattle'
'No mockeries now for them'
No deathbed confessions
Only prayers on the prevailing wind.

Unseen the reaper hard at work.
The funeral pyre, it burns for thee
My friend, and the cattle bell
It tolls for thee as well.

The culled dairy herd lying in the silage clamp,
Ramscliffe Farm, Beaford, North Devon

77

Washing down after the cull, Ramscliffe Farm,
Beaford

A CLEANSING OPERATION

No sun can bleach the soul
of what we have seen,
the unspoken truth
which sits upon our shoulders.

Gobsmacked and in a daze
men in spacesuits walk around
as if there has been a chemical attack
the air reeks of disinfectant.

Clean round the bend.

After the cull—MAFF employees disinfecting before
leaving the farm, Ramscliffe, Beaford

ENTRY PROHIBITED

The virus, of course, cannot read
It has no degree in microbiology
But jumps barriers all the same,

Keeps vets on their toes, as surely
As any racehorse will,
With the wind under its tail.

Accusations and theorems
Fly across the night sky,
Like tracer over Baghdad.

Under siege … *La Peste* …
The Pestilence rampant.
Camus was right, the Visitations,

The Plagues of Egypt,
As yet another farm is brought to its knees.
Border guards stand guard implacably,

Only they are not sure what it is they are looking for.
The invisible double agent
That has already given them the slip.

HALT WHO GOES THERE ?
Only disinfectant,
Exhausted vets and a plague of locusts.

THE AFTERMATH

And after it is all over
Reports are written by eminent men

Inquiries take their toll
With carefully chosen words

That somehow dance around the 'truth'
That no one in particular is to blame

Or that the truth is well and truly buried
Like the animals themselves.

Vaccinate or vacillate?
Bodies and antibodies.

Speechless, the virus
Always seems to have the last word.

Ramscliffe Farm—Post Cull

THE SILENT ALTAR

To cull or not to cull?
That is the delicate question
Which rivets the countryside,
Into a steel hull,

Vaccinating it against
The slow internal machinations,
Inexplicable delays, bureaucracy
Which dogs us at every step.

Lives are at stake, good husbandry
Counts for nothing in this game,
Only the need to understand a clock
That cannot be turned back.

The spring has snapped,
Centuries of common sense
And stockmanship
Snuffed out in a twinkling.

Small things others would not notice,
Ridge and furrow in the evening light,
Farmers and their families sacrificed
On the silent altar of barren fields.

Covered produce sign, Ramscliffe Farm,
Beaford, North Devon

FMD 2

Carcasses breed carcasses
The never ending ring of fire
Encircling whole villages
In its black, awful, oily grasp,

The obligatory smokescreen
That strides down the valley
Obscures reality,
As if a whole fleet is on manoeuvres.

The awful pit wrenching smell
Magnified a thousand times
Stifles conversation, deadens the land
Breeds its own intricate language.

'Render unto Caesar what is Caesar's'
Trench warfare, digging in, time flies,
Seen but not herd, the silent wake
Buried deep in the countryside.

Beltane has come early this year,
Dead cattle driven through the flames.
Sacrifice to an unnamed God.
Celtic solution: Wicca Man.

Preparing the pyre, Ramscliffe Farm,
Beaford, North Devon

Some days after the cull Philip Lake telephoned to say that the Ministry were going to burn his animals at Ramscliffe on Easter Sunday, along with others from neighbouring farms. I was very welcome to come and take some photographs. But I had already decided that as a family we could no longer take the strain. It was mostly my own fault, for I had become im-mersed in the crisis to the point of obsession, and keeping it from my neighbours had not been easy. But where could we go?

The Isles of Scilly are a favourite place of ours, so I rang the islands' Tourist Board. Yes, they were open for business. Did it matter that we would be coming from a FMD infected area? No, we have no restrictions, but visitors must go through a dis-infectant footbath on arrival, both at the harbour and the airport. And what about footpaths, could we walk? No problems there, all the footpaths are open. The swift replies came as a bit of a shock Over the last few weeks I'd become used to a world of obstruction and strict regulation. We were so delighted we immediately booked return flights

ESCAPE AND RETURN

from Penzance (no rolling around on the Scillonian ferry for me!) and a family room at a guesthouse on St Mary's.

Once settled on the island it seemed our troubles were over. We bought maps and planned an itiner-ary. We would walk the coast of St Mary's and on another day catch a boat to Tresco, a delightful sub-trop-ical island famous for its gardens and tranquillity.

On our first morning we walked into the town, and that one simple pleasure lifted our spirits. We bought provisions for a picnic and hired a taxi. I asked the driver to take us to the northern tip of the island so that we could walk back along the coast path. The day was cold but pleasant, and our son was excited and full of beans. But it was on this drive, passing hedgerow and field, that the nightmare of the past few weeks came flooding back. And I was curious, where were the island's livestock?

Our driver told us that tourism was now by far the greatest earner for the archipelago, and livestock rearing and even the famous daffodil industry had taken a back seat.

'They closed the abattoir some years back and the cost of taking livestock to the mainland to be slaughtered made it uneconomical. It's a lot more profitable farming tourists!'

The next few days passed quickly. We ate well and took plenty of exercise and the mini break did us all the world of good, but once rejuvenated I was eager to get back to Ramscliffe. It wasn't that I felt guilty. There had been so many pictures of burning pyres, both in the newspapers and on television, that I had convinced myself that missing the burn at Ramscliffe would not jeopardise the story. Nevertheless I needed some proof that I was right.

On a beautiful sunny day I returned to the farm. Philip was in good spirits and glad that the burn was behind him. Out in the field the long neat rows of the pyre were still smouldering and so I wandered up and down with my camera, scanning each side, trying to make sense of the piles of ash. And then I saw it. There, lying amongst the fire-shattered bones was a fetlock, still with bits of hide stuck to it, and attached to the charred remains, a lone cow's hoof.

When I looked through the camera this image struck me as extremely poignant, especially as I hadn't expected to come across it. I have never been to war but the smouldering pyre blocking out the spring sunshine, together with the symbol of the hoof, took on the mantle of a huge tragedy. This picture would bring home the appalling waste of the last few weeks. I wasn't going to need burning cows.

Redundant milking parlour, Ramscliffe Farm,
Beaford, North Devon

PYROTECHNICS

It reminds me of Varanasi
And the burning ghats.
Only there is no Ganges
Flowing to the sea,

No sweet smelling incense,
No priests with bells.
Only a deep dark pit.
Fat, offal, skin and bones.

Sacred cows broken down
Into muscle spasms
As the blethering heat
Takes hold of the herd.

Barbecue time as Kali dances.
Smoke screens unveiled.
An offering to the god
Of political necessity.

The Raw and the Cooked,
The Origin of Table Manners,
Another family left teetering
On the edge of madness.

Smouldering pyre, Ramscliffe Farm,
Beaford, North Devon

In order to keep my vehicle well disinfected I had chanced on a service at the Okehampton Training Camp and just seven miles from home. I knew some of the men manning the entrance to the military road on the moor and they were quite happy to spray my vehicle. But I never let on where I was going.

One evening, after an exhausting day driving around the battered countryside, the poet James Crowden and I drove up onto this northern flank of Dartmoor. James had worked as both farm labourer and shepherd and I had wanted him to witness the extent of the tragedy. There are good views to be had across the vast region of North Devon and as the sun went down we began to count the number of smouldering pyres. There were thirteen in all. We turned and looked at each other, both grinning sarcastically; 'So Mr Blair, the countryside is open for business?' We felt he ought to come and take a look.

That same day we had visited Beaford and met Percy Lake. He'd taken us out on to the road leading to Beaford Moor to show us the results of yet another cull. Across the fields a long line of dead sheep lay under a hedge looking for all the world like the last vestiges of snow soon after a thaw. 'It's disgusting' said Percy,' they've been lying around for days. The birds are picking away at them. Surely that will spread disease?'

POSTCARDS

After what the Lakes had been through you could understand Percy's anger and frustration but it had been clear for some time that the sheer numbers being culled had overtaken the rate of disposal. On the same day that Ramscliffe was culled MAFF received the approval to bury up to half a million animals in a mass grave at Ash Moor, on the edge of a clay pit just north of Hatherleigh. With the backlog of slaughtered animals reaching well over 30,000 there was now deep concern at the number of pyres that would be needed. There was also the perceived risk that the disease could spread across the countryside on the thermal currents created by the burning of carcasses that did have the virus. Engineering work began at Ash Moor on the 9th April although there was a great deal of local protest. Initially access to the site was through

Felling a line of oak trees on the edge of
Ash Moor Pit, Petrockstowe, Devon

a narrow private road and hopelessly inadequate. A long line of mature oaks was felled in preparation but a new access was then granted via the entrance to the clay works at Meeth on the A386. By the 12th April there were 110,000 slaughtered animals awaiting disposal; by the 15th the figure had risen to over 130,000; four days later the figure stood at 167,000 and was described by the National Farmers' Union as a 'disgraceful situation'.

A number of animals were also being slaughtered on the Livestock Welfare Disposal Scheme. The Hardings, our farming neighbours, had experienced the first exodus of perfectly healthy sheep under the scheme, which of course could not go to market. The Ministry would not tell John where the sheep were going, but the lorry driver did. It seemed a landfill site had been chosen on the Ugbrooke Estate between Chudleigh and Kingsteignton. John thought it a terrible waste.

Outside the town of Holsworthy a huge burning area had also been constructed to cope with the backlog. On the day that it was lit James and I made a visit hoping to get a picture. We found that the best vantage point was in a lane running along the bottom of the valley below the disposal site. But it was already filled with the media. We watched for some time as a female presenter rehearsed her piece to camera whilst tossing and combing her hair. It was bizarre. This was springtime in Devon, bathed in promising sunshine, yet in the distance a sulphurous ash filled cloud was creeping towards her across the fields. Without knowing why, you would have been forgiven for thinking that Holsworthy was at war.

You didn't have to look hard to find other clues to the tragedy. One weekend my wife Helen and I were invited out to dinner in North Devon and on our way home the car headlights lit up a pile of dead sheep lying in a corner of a field against the road. I instinctively knew it would make a picture. During the summer this stretch of road, close to the North Tawton cheese factory, is ablaze with the colour of corn and had often caught my eye. The road twists, dips and turns across a gentle undulating landscape towards Dartmoor, with its distinctive hill of Cosdon Beacon in the distance. At the crack

Protest signs at the entrance to Ash Moor Pit,
Meeth, Devon

THE DISEASE

It sprints down motorways,
Seeps across county boundaries,
Does not respect the niceties
Of parish maps or tribal status.

Long lines of fires,
Beacons for a new cargo cult,
Carcasses, legs outstretched
Stare up at the pecked sky

Food for ravens and crows.
Fox and badger skulk,
Gluttony on a vast scale,
Burnt offerings to The Ministry,

Bamboozled by their own bureaucracy.
Veterinary knowledge is sidelined,
Vectors unconfirmed, riding on the wind
Mathematical modelling taken to extremes.

King for a day, election fever
The blanket kill, panic at the top.
The virus of spin, spinning out of control
Political necessity a bitter pill to swallow.

Lorry loads of sleepers move at night,
Make the journey run more smoothly,
An invisible railroad across the farm,
Swiftly banked, the five figure cheque.

View from the Winkleigh Road looking
towards Dartmoor,

TOURISM

Bread and butter
One hell of a picnic
Sandwiched between spin.

The countryside
Is open for business.

Spring on Dartmoor,
Brent Tor car park closed to the public

99

of dawn I donned my overalls and the essential flat cap and drove back to where I had seen the sheep. But as I slowed I caught sight of a policeman sat in his car, blocking the entrance to the farm opposite. He stared straight at me.

With a friendly smile I gave him a wave and drove on, convinced he wasn't local and would take me for a farmer out on his rounds. A mile up the road I turned the vehicle round. I could see the sheep in the distance and I wanted that picture! I waited awhile and then drove back, acknowledging the policeman again, but as soon as I was out of his sight I pulled up sharp. There could be no hanging around. I ran across the road, clambered on to the bank to mimic the view from my car and fired off a number of frames. It was a grey sombre morning and the light was poor, but I had my picture.

Pleased with the success of my mission I decided not to go home but instead drove into the centre of Okehampton. It was a Sunday morning and by this time the skies were clearing for a cold but promising day. But the air, pulled in through the vents in my car, stank. I soon discovered why.

On the other side of town MAFF had lit a pyre on a farm just below Meldon Dam on the northwest edge of the moor. The light southwesterly wind was taking the smoke down the valley, across the A30 dual carriageway and straight into town. Later a friend recalled how he had arrived back at his flat on the Saturday evening with his new girlfriend, who had flown over from Holland to join him for the week. 'We woke on the Sunday morning to bright sunshine and I flung open the windows to let in what should have been the fresh spring air of Dartmoor. It didn't impress her! We nearly choked! What a stench! The whole town was covered with a sickly, light smog.'

Fortunately for them, the wind swung round later in the morning.

On another occasion, driving up to Torrington, I spotted a long line of feeding troughs snaking across a field empty of livestock. It was a perfect spring day with azure blue skies and cotton wool clouds. It should have been a beautiful sight, the farmed Devon landscape at its very best, but in fact there wasn't a sheep, lamb or cow to be seen right through to the horizon. And there in the distance to the right of the farm was the tell-tale burning pyre.

I must emphasise that these were all pictures that anyone could have taken from the road. They were not hidden away from the tourist. I called them my Devon postcards, postcards from Hell and if I had thought they would have got through to him, I would have sent them to Mr Blair.

Spring in Devon, 2001. View from the A386 towards Lovistone Barton, Huish

Some humour is needed to alleviate the otherwise miserable happenings of 2001 and whilst I wish to offer my own conclusions on this sorry affair, I am reminded of a rather silly situation that arose on Dartmoor, which both amused and lifted our spirits.

CONCLUSION

It was on 6th June 2001, to great relief and applause, that all footpaths and bridle-ways across South Dartmoor were re-opened. However to our surprise the region to the north remained closed and in order to implement this all lay-bys to the north of the B3212, which literally bisects the moor, were cordoned off with temporary chestnut fencing, together with a distinctive red sign informing the public that the north of the moor was strictly a no-go area. A maximum fine of £5,000 was in place if you ignored it. On the opposite side of the road, marked by a green sign, all lay-bys were open, with unrestricted access onto the moor. Here you could picnic, walk, fly a kite and stand on your head.

To an outsider this may have seemed both logical and appropriate. Close half the moor nearest to the outbreaks and open the rest to recreation.

But to those of us living on the moor the scheme was nothing more than half-baked. It is impossible to close one half of open moorland. And it soon became apparent that some of the inhabitants of Dartmoor were showing utter contempt for the law.

Out on the commons the sheep, in whose interest this rule had been implemented, were happily grazing in their time-honoured way—wandering aimlessly, unaware of their crime, and criss-crossing the road to both areas of moor.

Our ability to make the wrong decisions in a time of crisis is a symptom of human frailty and whilst the above is forgivable, the handling of the crisis is not. The lessons learnt from the last major outbreak in 1967 should have prompted successive governments to have on standby a contingency plan for emergency vaccination. MAFF claims they had one, and if so then much criticism can be levelled that it wasn't implemented immediately. It is true that under a European Union directive dating from 1992 the use of wholesale vaccination to combat FMD was prohibited. This was to protect the member state's position as a 'disease free' region thus protecting its international trading status and its valuable world export market in meat. However when FMD broke out in Holland in April 2001, the Dutch immediately ring-vaccinated their outbreaks and then later agreed to slaughter all the animals. The strategy was a success. FMD was stamped out and within three months Holland had regained its export status. (There are many who would argue that there was of course no need to slaughter the vaccinated animals. The slaughter was ordered simply to regain export status as soon as possible. It would have taken twelve months had the animals lived.)

This drive to protect export markets was certainly a priority for many associated with the industry. What is clear from all of this is that MAFF was steeped in a culture of anti-vaccination regarding this particular disease. It is interesting to note that we routinely vaccinate sheep and cattle against many harmful diseases, including blackleg and lamb pneumonia, and dysentery in pigs. Provided there is a safe withdrawal period, milk and meat from these vaccinated animals enters the food chain without challenge.

Foot and Mouth is seen, quite rightly, as one of the worst threats in existence to animal health, but to have ignored the benefits of emergency vaccination purely on economic grounds shows a lack of compassion for animal welfare and to many of us was morally wrong. The Ministry of Agriculture had access to proof that emergency vaccination, coupled with the slaughter of the infected animals, can be a highly successful strategy. In 1996 FMD broke out in Macedonia in an area about the same size as Devon. Promoted and supported by the European Union, 120,000 cattle were vaccinated and 4,500 destroyed. Outbreaks from the type-A virus were eliminated within three weeks.

But Britain would not go down this route. The government was standing firm and sticking to the tried and tested policy of rapidly slaughtering all confirmed outbreaks and disposing of the carcasses.

On the 11th of March the Agricultural Minister, Nick Brown, was questioned about the handling of the crisis in an interview with Sir David Frost. He was asked if it was now under control? 'We do have it under control—we are eliminating it'. But the phone lines to the programme immediately became jammed. People on the ground had a different story to tell. The government's assurance that all animals with confirmed disease were being slaughtered within 24 hours was not being met.

And it was no wonder. Farming had changed dramatically since the last outbreak. There were now at least twice as many sheep in the country, they were marketed earlier, they moved faster and more frequently, and they travelled further. In 1967 the primary outbreak was reported before infected animals left the farm. The current outbreak had a head start by not being recognised until it reached a slaughterhouse and by then the virus, mainly through the rapid movement of sheep, was being dispersed nationally. As each day brought new cases MAFF was facing a logistical nightmare. Instead of being on top of the disease they were simply chasing it and although they refused to admit it, they hadn't the resources to handle the magnitude of the epidemic.

With MAFF in turmoil a group of top-level scientists, led by Professor Roy Anderson, a scientist who had used computers in the past to plot the course of BSE, were eagerly waiting in the wings. They were desperate to present their advice on how to tackle the disease. Sanctioned and organised by Sir John Krebs, the head of the Food Standards Agency, a meeting with MAFF was arranged. The presentation by the scientists was opened by Dr Neil Ferguson of Imperial College London. With the data the team had available Ferguson showed by a computer generated graph what could happen if the disease, with its present level of control by MAFF, was allowed to run its course. It was predicted that by the beginning of May up to 1,000 farms a day could become infected.

The Chief Veterinary Officer, Jim Scudamore, was not impressed though he had to admit the situation was dire. But Professor David King, the Government's Chief Scientific Advisor, was also at the meeting. Over the next few days, in a series of deft political moves, Jim Scudamore was sidelined and Anderson's team effectively put in charge.

During the presentation Neil Ferguson had also put forward a plan to combat the frightening predictions. He stated that if you wanted to bring the disease under control it was imperative that all animals contracting the disease were slaughtered within 24 hours and to stop further spread of disease a ring cull of animals around the hotspot should be carried out within 48 hours. The seed was sown for the contiguous cull.

On the 23rd March it was David King who went on television to announce the new nationwide policy. A last ditch attempt was made to persuade Tony Blair that there was another way.

Prince Charles was constantly in touch with Downing Street and was a strong ally for the pro-vaccination lobby. On hearing the evidence put forward in a paper written by Lawrence Woodward from the Elm Farm Research Centre, Tony Blair, with an election looming, came close to adopting a strategy for vaccination. Woodward was invited to a meeting at Downing Street. He outlined his plan for ring vaccination but was told by David King that it wasn't practical. He was informed that there were only about 175,000 cattle doses of vaccine available. Woodward said later: 'I got the distinct impression that it was only the day before that they had begun to look for new supplies of vaccine.' However, Blair did sanction a more limited strategy, agreeing to vaccinate all dairy cows in Cumbria that were about to come out on to spring pasture. He would leave it to Nick Brown to persuade the farmers. But later Blair was out-manoeuvred by his agricultural minister. At a meeting at the Ministry Nick Brown offered the farmers' leaders a vote on the issue, giving them the option to leave the cows indoors. The option to vaccinate was buried.

For me, and I imagine for a great many others, the contiguous cull was the most damning element of the whole crisis. If the scientists had been on the farms of Huccaby and Ramscliffe they may well have altered the forecasts drawn from their computers. The claim of possible disease incubation in animals on farms close to an outbreak was not proved. Without vaccination no doubt it was a sensible policy to kill dangerous contacts swiftly and efficiently with the quick disposal of carcasses paramount, but just what constituted a dangerous contact? The cattle at Huccaby never came into contact with those at Dunnabridge. Philip Lake's dairy herd at Ramscliffe was separated from the outbreak on his cousin's farm by a main road. I was there when the vet examined the animals after the cull. All were free from any clinical signs of disease. To kill so many fit and healthy animals that were contiguous simply because they fell within a three kilometre radius, and especially when in many cases two weeks and more had passed by with no sign of the disease, was to my mind seriously flawed. Vets that I talked to felt the risk of transmission was zero after this period of time had elapsed. The rise in temperature with the onset of summer, coupled with the fact that most of the infected hotspots had been stamped on, was a more likely reason for the curtailment in the spread of disease.

During the crisis some criticism for the rapid spread of the disease was laid at the door of the farmer and whilst I have always championed the industry it would be wrong of me not to mention the abuse of the annual ewe premium, a subsidy established by the European Union in 1980. Known as the Sheepmeat Regime, it had been implemented to ensure a fair standard of living for producers and to help stabilise the market. Without it most sheep farmers would make a loss. But this payment could be claimed on ewes whether they produced lambs or not, and behind the scenes a black market had inevitably evolved.

A farmer would register a claim in November, but it wasn't until the following February that those same sheep might be counted by MAFF inspectors. There is no doubt in many people's minds that some farmers in the early spring of 2001 were either borrowing or purchasing sheep, often of inferior quality, in order to satisfy their previous claim on quota. Livestock dealers must have played their part. Cull ewes could be bought at market very cheaply, and their traceability thereafter was very difficult to ascertain as MAFF was to discover soon after the outbreak. And however uncomfortable this sounds, some proof of the scam was highlighted in the *Farmers Weekly* in July 2001. In Northern Ireland, when the Ministry compared the numbers culled during the FMD outbreak in South Armagh with the numbers claimed for the annual subsidy, the figures just didn't match. Of the 93 farmers who had claimed, over half of them had fewer sheep than they needed to meet their claims, and 16 had no sheep at all! Some 3,187 sheep had gone 'missing'. Similar discrepancies were found in other parts of the province. Borrowing sheep in case an inspector calls is known as 'bed and breakfasting'. If ever there was a system open to abuse, this was it.

The Foot and Mouth crisis also highlighted the chronic problem of illegal entry of meat products into this country, but an analysis of the situation leads one to sympathise with the mammoth task of trying to police it. How many of us have returned from holidays abroad and walked straight through the green channel at customs without challenge? The sheer volume of human traffic would need huge resources if we were to ever come near to a strict regime of baggage checking. And discovering meat products hidden in consignments on board containers and lorries coming into port is an equally daunting task for both Customs and Port Health Authority staff.

In May 2002 Bobby Waugh was convicted on nine charges out of a total of sixteen brought against him. These consisted of incidents of animal cruelty and of covering up the disease on his farm. He was also convicted of one count of feeding unprocessed waste to his animals and one of failing to properly dispose of animal by-products. He has been banned from keeping animals.

The way in which Waugh conducted his business was an absolute disgrace and has brought shame on his profession. In my thirty-year career as a photographer I have come across similar scenes of poor husbandry, but the incidents have been rare. It is an inescapable fact that it is always the minority who let the side down, so tarnishing the industry's reputation.

Silence at Ramscliffe is not the definitive record of how it was in the Devon countryside of 2001, but the story, pictures and poetry are offered as testimony to the agony, so often overlooked, that was experienced by many and from all walks of life. A certain amount of faith has to be vested in any elected government but I believe that in this case we were thoroughly let down.

Professor Ian Mercer, the independent chairman for Devon County Council's public inquiry, expressed it well in *Crisis and Opportunity: Devon Foot and Mouth Inquiry 2001*:

'A thorough national and formal public inquiry (able to summon ex-Ministers and civil servants at all levels) would be a more appropriate process for holding central Government players to account. But, even then, the fencing of legal advocates and defenders could prolong, perplex and confuse the issues until the truth was even more buried than it is now. It is, after all, already quite clear that the outbreak and the handling of the ensuing crisis was lamentable.'

It most certainly was.

THE END

Half open—half closed, Dartmoor, June 2001

An interview with Philip Lake on the 30th August 2001 at Ramscliffe Farm, Beaford, North Devon

It was the toughest twelve months I've ever known in farming. It was getting us down. We were getting really, really fed up with the weather. It was a wet summer the year before and then a wet winter. And then Foot and Mouth came along and we had all the movement restrictions.

Nigel and Geoffrey Lake, my cousins up at Brealeys, were the first to get it in Beaford. Before that it was about five miles away at Iddisleigh. There was a worry, but we never thought it was going to reach us. Nigel had been down in the morning after milking his cows. I remember we were joking, saying that because it was raining every day we wished we'd get Foot and Mouth, not for a minute thinking we would. I came in that evening to a message on the answerphone saying they'd got it. It was a total shock.

We carried on as normal as possible. Any vehicle that came in and out was disinfected. We had 105 milkers and about an average of 90 of those would be milking all the time. Then there was over 100 young stock on the farm, in-calf heifers, store cattle and some calves.

Ramscliffe owns 188 acres and we rent a further 60 or so. The farm's about 250 acres in all. Our main interest was dairy and then rearing on beef calves plus replacement heifers. We did the milk round because we were involved with the Definitely Devon factory at Torrington. We've got a financial involvement in the factory. Definitely Devon is a co-operative formed about four years ago. There are about 48 farmers involved. We re-opened a factory that was closed by the Government and went into processing. We all put some money up and the European Commission gave some 5B [rural redevelopment] funding and off we went. It came about because we were finding it hard selling our milk to the factories. They were becoming too dominant. But since we've had the factory we've found the supermarkets are just the same, so it's no easier! The factory produces milk, butter, soft cheese and clotted cream. It's still up and running but hard work.

POSTSCRIPT

Philip Lake on the day they re-stocked,
Ramscliffe Farm, Beaford, North Devon

The difference between now and Father's day is the cost of living, and the drop in milk price. In the mid-nineties we were booming, no question, but then it dropped 10p a litre which to me was a drop of £65,000 in profit! We were making over a thousand pounds a week, and although there was tax it was good. Last year, although we haven't had the accounts yet, I can tell you now that we will probably have made a loss. If everything had stayed balanced when we were getting 22p a litre things would have been fine. But it shot up to 26p for a while and then dropped right back to 16p. The only ones who could make any money were the ones who were very efficient with these two or three hundred cow herds. I couldn't do that. I wouldn't have the room to move. And I wouldn't want to.

The milking was a tie. When we were making money, I enjoyed it. I loved it. But for what we were earning I was beginning to feel tied to it. If you had your wages cut in half you wouldn't have the incentive to go to work, would you?

It was April 6th when they took us out: 216 cattle and 22 sheep.

After the cull it was such a change. In a way it was an exciting time. We were very busy most of the time right up until a week ago. Cleaning the farm and re-thinking. We finished the clean-up here at the end of July but only finished the buildings off the farm last Friday. The compensation was tremendous, there's no two ways about that and was twice as good as a sale. It was a good way out of a bad situation although it's not the way you would choose obviously. But when you think that you've still got all your property, all your quota, all your machinery, it's only the stock that's gone. And the clean-up money was good.

But in fact it has changed me mentally. Before Foot and Mouth we were borrowers and you would go out and borrow money for machinery or whatever. But now I'm an investor I make do. You have got the money invested and come hell or high water you want to keep it! The compensation was high but my feeling all the way through this was that the Government doesn't want to have so many farmers and this was the pay off. And don't forget that there will be a long period without any income. It sounds a lot but it's not really.

I've been looking at other things, diversification and looking into the grants and trying not to go back to such intensive farming. I took out the milking parlour. If I had gone back into milking I would have needed a new one. It had got too old and there was no sale value in the parts. The bulk tank will fetch something because that one is nearly new.

I had a mind to start up with horses. I employed a manager and thought about a riding school. But when we tried to get the grants we found it was going to be a hassle, and when we really started to look into it, the upkeep with what we were going to get out of it meant that we'd only just about break even. So we called it a day. And there were too many people around as well. No privacy! I know some farmers have talked about going into the holiday business but I would not convert my barns unless I sold the lot and moved!

We've made a lot of big bale silage, which hopefully we can sell after Christmas. I think there will be a demand for it because there was a lot of stock on farms that were left in. They've also been carrying stock on fields that should have been cut. I know there's a lot of silage been made but if you go the other side of Exeter or onto Exmoor there's a lot of stock up there. There should be a demand for it, we'll wait and see. Or maybe we will re-stock ourselves.

I can re-stock on November 1st but I'm in no hurry because the outbreaks are still carrying on. These Northumberland outbreaks are worrying. Once in a lifetime is enough! But I would like to buy some sheep in and have them running around. I've always done that—had a few store lambs. It was one of the few things that paid this last year.

I don't know of anyone who is going back into dairy. There was only one farm that escaped in Beaford and everyone else seems to be just drifting and waiting for an opportunity. It's a good arable area around here and I think a lot of land will be put down to corn. Traditionally it has been dairy and stock farms and the fertility is there in the soil.

I don't know what the future is—you tell me. The ones who seriously stay in farming will have to go big—two or three hundred dairy cows and a couple of thousand sheep. I've got three daughters so I don't feel I need to go back into serious farming.

I can muddle along. Do a bit of arable, beef and sheep. But I couldn't walk away from farming completely. It's in my blood. I've had periods when I've had nothing to do throughout this Foot and Mouth business and I've become incredibly bored and bad tempered. I think everyone needs a challenge both physical and mental … we shall see.

Pre-slaughter, Philip Lake with his cows,
Ramscliffe Farm, Beaford, North Devon

THE GUIDED TOUR

Percy said he'd take us to the spot
Barely visible from the road,
A long white line jumbled up
Just this side of the hedge, three fields in.

You could pick them out with binoculars
Ten feet thick the line,
Bits of wool blowing in the wind.
A thousand sheep, slaughtered.

And then you get the binoculars in focus
Pick out lambs amongst the carnage.
Percy says the other farm by the trees
Had it bad, these at least were healthy.

The word 'contiguous' slips off his tongue
With accustomed ease,
As if it was a favourite Roman Emperor
Or a new type of Four Wheel Drive:

The Ford 'Contiguous'. The off-road cull.
Then swing the glasses to the left
A horizontal blur, black, white and brown
Hundreds of cattle laid out in low mounds

As if some ceremony was about to take place.
"Killed yesterday. They'll burn next week"
Percy hands the glasses back,
Nods and smiles philosophically,

As if he was following the hunt,
Re-adjusts his well thumbed cloth cap.
Percy's a bit of an expert now
His son's farm was taken out last week.

BEAFORD AND BEYOND

'And the other animals on the hill?
He's fighting the Ministry through the courts
He won't win,
The smoke always runs up the valley.

And then there's the deer
They're dopey in the wood,
Lame and frothing
That's bad when it gets into the roe deer.

You never know when it'll come back.
Last time we had Foot and Mouth
That was 1952, near Ashreigney.
They killed them on the farm

And buried on the same day,
Loads of lime. That was that.
No spread. Quarantine
And disinfectant. End of problem.

We're disinfecting the farm now
Under our own steam.
Don't get me wrong
We didn't have it.

Milk round in the morning
Then the vets moved in at eleven.
That was it. Philip had to go inside.
Only a week between cull and burn.

Not bad really. The pyre's still
Smouldering. You can see it there.
But the silence gets to you
And what shall us do with all the grass?'

An interview with Percy and Roma Lake, Shepherds Meadow, Beaford, North Devon

Percy:

I was born in 1929 at Bakers Farm in Torrington, one of four boys. My parents were tenant farmers. In 1941 we moved from what was a 100-acre farm to a 250-acre farm in Beaford. John Puddicombe who was bailiff for the Clinton Estate over at Merton owned the farm but had got too old to run it so he let it to my parents.

During the war we had ten men working on the farm, and always plenty to do. My father did a milk round in Torrington, we kept a lot of sheep, two or three hundred, tilled a lot of corn, about seventy acres of corn. That was a lot of corn back in those days and my God it took some harvesting! My father used to till a lot of roots, acres of mangolds and swedes and he'd fold the sheep on that, and then he'd grow the corn. It would be a rotation of four years. He'd plough up and have grass, then he would have a field of corn, then it would go into roots and then it would go back to corn again and then he'd grass seed it out. Very

little fertiliser then—mainly dung! That was organic food—not what they'm turning out today!

We'd grow a wack of potatoes, twelve acres of potatoes and very often us had got German prisoners and Italian prisoners to pick them up—we had the labour all right! They would work. We had the soldiers there looking after them—keeping guard on them. They'd work. Yes.

You ask anyone in Beaford; a farm to be proud of. He was a good farmer.

You know, Beaford when I was in my youth was a good place. There was about fifteen young chaps that lived in Beaford and we used to congregate in the reading room. We used to play snooker, table tennis, and toast some bread if us wanted to, and the pub was over the road and there wasn't one who used to go to the pub. And they was nearly all in agriculture. It was the good old days. One of my mates he rings up now, he's seventy-five now, and he'll ring me just to have a tale and a laugh about those times. Well, there.

Well, Beaford was once all agriculture. Now we've got the Arts Centre up there and there's a

Percy Lake on the day they re-stocked,
Ramscliffe Farm, Beaford, North Devon

117

printing place (Canns Down Press). I don't think Foot and Mouth affected the village a lot. There's only one or two agricultural workers in Beaford you see.

In 1952 Roma and I got married and we moved into Ramscliffe, which was a neighbouring farm. We were a mixed farm, sheep and cows. I used to milk about twelve cows, twice a day by hand. We put the milk up on the milk stand and the lorries would pick it up and take it to Torridge Vale. We had store cattle and back then we used to keep a lot of fowls, and you might not believe it but that would pay a man's wages back then. We could live and pay a man's wages from the chicken and that—well, it was different times altogether.

We put all the money back into the farm. But as it went on we had to increase. We bought in the milking machine and got more cows. I didn't have a Startomatic (Lister generator). I used to milk the cows with an engine that worked the vacuum. We had about 25 to 30 cows but that was enough back then. In the winter you couldn't scrape out the dung with a tractor, you had to throw it out with a fork

and very few had got front-end loaders for loading the dung after you threw it out!

We left the farm in 1988 but stayed in as partners. Philip took over the running of it.

BSE was a terrible thing. We didn't actually have it ourselves but we had three cows that got it that were bought in. All the time they were blaming farmers, but it wasn't the farmers, it was the merchants who were mixing this meal and cake and stuff. We weren't aware of what was going into the feed. They never put that on the ticket when they brought the cake! But I have to say, Thomas's where we bought our cake, they didn't mix this bone and meat in the feed but there was another who did, and a lot of their customers had BSE.

As it went on we were having to keep too much stock to make a living. And everything seemed to be getting on top of people. The slurry problem and all that there. It was a nightmare. A lot of people didn't know what to do with the slurry and stuff. That was a headache. We were keeping more and more but standing still. It was partly due to losing the Milk Marketing Board I think. The first couple of years after it went there was a hell of a good price for milk, then all of a sudden, bang, it went down. That's where it went wrong, then. It never recovered from that. The feed, the labour was going up and the market value was going down. And we didn't really get much subsidy, we'd given up the sheep and increased the cows—but that made more slurry!

Then this Foot and Mouth. I think it's caused by all this foreign meat coming into the country and that swill, it wasn't boiled right, well it wasn't boiled enough was it? Years ago we'd take our animals in Torrington market and they'd end up down at North Devon Meat, most of it, and be killed down there. And that's about as far as your animals would go. And now they're bringing in meat from Brazil and Argentina, where they've got Foot and Mouth, and now it's pretty rife. Well it shouldn't be. What the hell was Blair and them thinking about, doing that? They're now saying that the farmers should take out insurance policies to cover this Foot and Mouth in future, well who's going to put up insurance when they've got it coming into the country?

The day Foot and Mouth came to Beaford was terrible. Nigel, my nephew, who farms at Brealeys, had been down to Ramscliffe in the morning. It was a Sunday morning, the 18th of March. He often came down 'cause he'd lost his father recently. That was my brother, Harold. Well, he stayed there talking in the milking parlour. He went from there over to Simmons's and stayed chatting with they for a while, which he always did, and in the afternoon, about six o'clock, he ringed up and you know he was in tears, he broke down. 'Us got it', he said 'us got it'. We couldn't believe it, no …

Well, although the main road separated us at the top of our lane, that right hand field, well that was full of sheep belonging to Brealeys. They shot them and left them in the corner. Left them there nearly a fortnight. Well, I had to ask them in the end to cover them up 'cause the birds and different things were going in there. Well, it was right on our doorstep, couldn't have been tighter. But there, we never had it. And they didn't come to see us for a fortnight, yeah, never came for a fortnight. Never rang up or nothing! That's what we couldn't get over. And then they came down and had a look around but we didn't have it. Nothing made sense. They killed Richard Snell's over at Middle Barlington a week before us, yet he was the next farm on from us going towards Roborough!

Well, we knew ours would have to go. It was the worst of the lot, the waiting. There was calves being born all the time, in fact we did shoot one or two, 'twas Friesian bull calves and there was no point in letting them live just to be shot by them. We done it before so that wasn't hard. You couldn't sell them.

Well, it was a relief when they were culled. We were so anxious. You see they'd be all right in the evening but the next morning you didn't know what you'd find. And food was getting short—that was the biggest trouble, that and the slurry.

But I don't know what the future is. At the moment I don't think there is a future for farming. A lot of our neighbours feel the same. The Simmons, lovely people, good neighbours, they went in there when we went in Ramscliffe. They were like us, young and full of ambition. Mr Simmons he was 80 the other day so John said. They still don't know what they're going to do. John's got two sons, just gone twenty, but they don't want to go back into milk, it's too much of a tie. And Richard Snell over at Middle Barlington, Philip said he told him he's definitely not going back into milk. He's got young sons. Corn, that what he's going to do. Looks like it, unless these animals improve. There's no money in sheep or beef. A thirty month old, well once it gets to thirty month old it could be worth £700 one minute and £260 the next! Well …

But you know I think milk will come back good. There's so many going out and there's not many youngsters coming into agriculture. I think milk will be good. And this organic, that's going to be a dead duck! This organic, a lot of it isn't organic. You go in Sainsbury's or Tesco's they've got organic oranges, they've got everything. Get out, it isn't organic. That was what was organic on my father's place. I don't go nothing on it!

What you want is stuff straight from the ground, stuff that hasn't travelled. Local. That's what you want.

And Philip? Well he says he'd rather go out to work than milk the cows again. It surprised me when he said that. But all the writing attached to the cows, all that paperwork, it was that that killed it. He was cheesed off with that before the Foot and Mouth come. That's what 'ave killed farming in the last few years, the paperwork.

He thought he would go into horses but that's now fallen through. There were too many rules and regulations with that. You're dealing with the public a lot, which he's not used to, and children and women! And the insurance was colossal.

So he's plodding along. He's talking about tilling a lot of corn next year. We shan't stock up until the spring although he may buy some store hogs, if you can. He'll buy some store bullocks in the spring and run they through the summer and fatten them out. He'll go along like that and with the milk round he should be able to make a living. We don't have to live off the farm because of our pensions so he should be all right. He coped with it terrific really, and there was a hell of a lot to cope with. He won't hurt.

Roma:

Our daughter was born in '54 and Philip was born in 1958. We only had the electricity when Philip was born. He was born in the January and we had the electric in just before Christmas. Before that it was the Tilly lights.

The wife was an important part of the farm. She took care of all the meals and we worked together as a unit. But these days the women go out to work. They have to I suppose with the cost of everything. It's sad to think about the way it's gone. People were more contented and happier I believe. We didn't have as much money but years ago the farmers, they all used to work together. You don't really notice the decline in things until something like this happens.

Next year we will have been married 50 years. If anyone had said to us a year ago that we were coming out of farming with this Foot and Mouth we'd have died there on the spot. But we've come to terms with it because we are out of it now. It's just Philip really. But he'll find a way forward.

Percy Lake and Mitchell Bright cleaning the
cubicles, Ramscliffe Farm, Beaford, North Devon

WHAT IT MEANS TO BE A FARMER
TRANSCRIBED HAND-WRITTEN LETTER FROM COLIN PEARSE

Barramoor Farm

North Bovey

Dartmoor

Devon

8th April 2005

Dear Chris

The problem with the post-traumatic stress, generated as a result of catastrophic events like Foot and Mouth, is that time has to move on, and things do go off the boil!

The urgency needed at the time to put in place aid, logistics and administration is forthcoming, but the final analysis doesn't always address the situation head on, and is found wanting.

It is brave of you, and necessary, that someone should maintain awareness of what Foot and Mouth did to families and farms and their animals, and indeed how whole communities and counties were affected at a stroke, instilling anxiety, causing isolation and even a depth of fear at losing a lifetime's work, often built on generations of dedication, pride and sheer graft.

This quite horrific disease resulted in the forced removal of millions of animals, many of which were burnt on the farm. 'Crossing the threshold of hope' seemed distant and unimaginable at the time!

Lessons seemed to have been learnt, but much of this was known before and never implemented, over-ruled by bureaucracy and not given the freedom of expression to highlight a better way forward for man and beast.

The 'burn-piles', lighting up the night time sky should never be allowed to happen again, or the indiscriminate removal of contiguous animals.

All this, in many cases on the farm where the animal was most likely to have been born and the farmer too; habitual, generative farming folk engaged in a mosaic farming scene of field, hedge, ditch and moor, and living with their animals, defending the age old practice of natural birth, giving dignity to their animals and offering countless care and sacrifice to achieve a meagre living. 'A continuous process of decision making in the face of uncertainty' often sustained by family succession, witnessing loyalty and a 'divine commitment' to livestock survival in the face of adversity.

There is a feeling of failure as the trust between guardian and animal is severed by 'force majeure'! Or was it insensitivity or even insensibility and unfeeling, or the match that was to try and destroy farming and the countryside alliance, leaving just a conical mound of ashes from which there could be no up-rising, plundering the 'life blood' of a livestock economy at its very heart?

Re-generation under normal circumstances is time honoured; a calf spending nine months in its mother's womb and a lamb five months. All this indicates to me fragility and something that can't be speeded up and requires experience, vigilance, faithfulness and a seven-day week, in the hope that the final timing and attention will achieve a living birth that can be nurtured with good husbandry for months and often years ahead, expanding the foundation of breeding stock and to supply a nation's food. These lives are a stockman's 'hallmark', portraying his courage and passion entrusted to him to help renew and foster tender life.

Well done Chris,

Good luck with your book.

Colin

The poet's view: the role of documentary poetry.

One evening in April 2001 I received a telephone call from the Devon photographer Chris Chapman. In guarded words he said that he had been given a commission by the Beaford Arts to document Foot and Mouth in North Devon. This was funded by Devon County Council who were keen that this bit of history should not go unrecorded. Chris had to work in utmost secrecy as access could easily have been refused. The work was very soul destroying and began with the cull at Dunnabridge in the middle of Dartmoor. A place I knew well. We had been out there recording a pony drift only the last autumn. Chris asked whether I would like to accompany him driving round Devon looking for photographs. I immediately jumped at this opportunity and went out with him for a couple of days. What I saw disturbed me greatly.

With so many culls, it felt as though we were documenting ethnic cleansing where odd villages or outlying farms were taken out one by one. It seemed as if Goya and Hieronymus Bosch were at our elbow, with endless pyres burning in the distance, so many pyres you lost count and it all became one long blur of grey smoke that crept into people's sitting rooms and lives. A blur that smelt horrendous, a smell that stayed with you for days and weeks. A mixture of coal, diesel, straw, wooden pallets, old railway sleepers and hundreds of tons of half burnt, putrefying flesh.

This poetry, which unashamedly reeks of war, is the result. The intensity and senselessness of the slaughter in the First World War came to mind immediately. All the poems were written at speed and within the week. Only a little editing has been done.

I make no apologies for that. Powerful images kept coming and are still coming. Certain borrowed lines and references are very obvious. There was nothing else that the experience could be linked to. Nothing like this has hit this country since the Blitz and that was in the cities, this was on farms and down peaceful rural lanes that William Cobbett and John Clare would have recognised. Like war photography, poetry in such circumstances is a necessary and sometimes dangerous art if people are to understand the full reality of what happened on their doorsteps. The greatest crime is that it should go unrecorded, that it should be forgotten. This is not the poetry of blame, only the poetry of grief and loss.

The sequence of poems and slides of the photographs called *Silence at Ramscliffe* were given their first public airing at 'Ways with Words'—The Dartington Literary Festival in July 2002. Then again in Manchester City Art Gallery to an assembly of Cumbrian vets and farmers, and more recently to history students at Bristol University. In each case the response from the audience was very marked. The cull had hit home. The enormity of what happened in that part of Devon and other areas of the country should never be underestimated. Foot and Mouth is horrendous but the policy of such wide contiguous culls of healthy animals was draconian. And there are still many questions to be answered about the mathematical modelling and the fact that high level veterinary wisdom was apparently sidelined in the interests of an impending election, lucrative export deals and spin doctoring. Vaccination can be debated till the cows come home.

These poems are in some sense political but more importantly they are rural. These events happened during spring and early summer when the hedgerow flowers were out. MAFF itself was formed in 1886 in response to an outbreak of Foot and Mouth in Lincolnshire infecting cattle which then went on into London. Ironically MAFF was abolished 115 years later in 2001 because of the same disease.

For many years I was a casual farm worker and shepherd. If I had been a farmer, a slaughterman, a vet or a government official, the poems would no doubt have had a slightly different slant. These are the poems of an interested and concerned observer. Some of them have already been featured in the *Western Morning News*. Many of the photographs appeared in the Devon County Council Foot and Mouth Report.

James Crowden
June 2005
www.james-crowden.co.uk

The researcher's view—the history of Foot and Mouth in Britain.

Significantly, Abigail Woods, one of the country's leading researchers on the history of Foot and Mouth disease, has highlighted the politics of response in the extracts below from her important book, *A Manufactured Plague*:

The calamitous re-appearance of Foot and Mouth Disease (FMD) in 2001 brought to the fore old questions about the nature of the disease, its means of spread and the best methods of controlling it. While unprecedented in its intensity, the shift to a wholesale cull policy was a logical extension of the traditional, century old method of FMD control. Hence, at the start of the 21st century, British FMD control was based upon the same principles as the measures introduced during the later 19th century, when Queen Victoria was Empress of India and the germ theory of disease had yet to be accepted....

Suspicions that Defra [Department for Environment, Food and Rural Affairs] intends to reapply its 2001 policy in future outbreaks were first aroused in autumn 2001, when it introduced a new Animal Health Bill, proposing legal power to enforce an extended cull. The bill confirmed critics' suspicions about the illegality of its actions during the 2001 epidemic. It was denounced in the House of Lords and defeated; but the government's large majority in the House of Commons ensured its passage in 2002. In their recent analysis of these events, University of Cardiff law professors David Campbell and Robert Lee complained 'The government, rather than review the flaws in its policy … is avoiding any lessons learned by purporting to give itself the legal power to repeat its mistakes … it is legislation which intentionally gives a power to panic.' …

Will Defra follow the example of the now defunct MAFF and stick stubbornly to a slaughter-only policy? Or will it make a new kind of history and adopt vaccination?

From the conclusion of A Manufactured Plague *by Abigail Woods, published by Earthscan 2004, pp. 146, 150, 151. Reproduced with permission.*

Footnote: On May 26, 2005, Defra's Deputy Chief Vet, Fred Landeg, revealed that the Government would not rule out using the contiguous cull policy in future FMD outbreaks, despite an independent modelling exercise, commissioned by Defra, which showed that using vaccination could cut the size of a major outbreak by half.

Counting sheep: animal casualties in Foot and Mouth by James Crowden.

Counting livestock is always a problem. Large beef and dairy animals are relatively easy to count. They stand still or come quietly into the parlour twice a day. Sheep are another matter and are often scattered over many miles of open country, gathered with dogs then slid past a narrow gap in the wall or a gateway. In the old days the shepherd stood there with a notched stick. Sheep counting systems are notoriously interesting and local. While shearing in Somerset, Dorset and Devon I often found the older shearers counting in scores. In the north of England, Cumbria has many variations on sheep counting. 1–10 is: yan, tyan, tethera, methera, pimp, sethera, lethera, hovera, dovera, dick. 15 was bumfit and 20 the score or mark on the stick. Accuracy in sheep counting at high speed was legendary and many fingers were brought into play.

It is interesting that the sheep counting systems that exist in Wales and Scotland also use the score as the final mark. Sheep are often sold at auction in pens of 20. Larger figures are simple additions: 3 and 15 is 18, 3 score and 10 is your lot, i.e. 70 years.

Often ewes are counted as couples, with one or two lambs at foot. In Wales I have seen black lambs left out of the equation altogether. Whether this is superstition is open to question. The term 'black sheep' has many resonances. Every family has one, or at least they used to in the good old days.

Defra or MAFF as it was then called, however uses an altogether different approach to livestock counting. Computer analysis has a more academic angle, or so it might seem, but there is no real substitute for a shepherd counting with his eyes and fingers.

In Devon there were 173 confirmed cases of Foot and Mouth (last Devon case 17th June 2001) But over 4,500 farms were put under MAFF Form D notices restricting movement of animals. With 10,500 farms in the county that is over 40 per cent of all farms in Devon affected in some way. The welfare problems were often as bad as Foot and Mouth disease itself and many animals suffered unnecessarily as Chris Chapman's diary records:

'There was a growing problem on many farms, including those some distance from a confirmed outbreak. Although you could move your cows down the road to be milked with a licence, no other livestock was allowed on the public highway. With the lambing season underway, this restriction threatened animal welfare. In my own parish our biggest sheep farmers, the Hardings, could not bring their pregnant ewes that were grazing elsewhere back to the farm to lamb, nor could they move off the farm sheep that had already given birth. This was causing considerable overcrowding.

Early one morning we awoke to an urgent banging at our front door. We opened it to find Rosemary Harding, looking very tired and clearly distraught. She pleaded with me to bring my camera, asking me if I would bear witness to what she said was an appalling scene.

It had been a cold, sharp night and some of their flock were in a small field some two and half miles from the shelter of the lambing sheds back home. The couple had been up all night, visiting the field at midnight and then again at three in the morning. Her husband, John, explained what had happened:

"When I turned the Land Rover into the field the headlights caught the eyes of a row of foxes up on the hedge. I knew what they were about but we had no choice. We lambed what we could and then went on to tend to others. We came back again at six o'clock and this is what we found."

Lying close to the hedge was a body of a ewe, together with that of her half born lamb. The birth sac was still upon the lamb's body, and clearly it had never had the chance to take its first breath. It was hard to tell whether or not the mother had been eaten alive, but her womb had been ripped open and her innards strewn about the field and chewed.

The anger and desperation on my neighbour's faces said it all. This was their livelihood, something that they were immensely proud of, and the movement restrictions were making it impossible for them to look after their stock in the way they knew best. All I could do was to sympathise and show pity, knowing that the scenes like this were probably being repeated on many a Westcountry farm. I went home feeling utterly sickened.'

Movement restrictions. John and Rosemary Harding
with overcrowded lambs, Murchington, Dartmoor

Figures of livestock slaughtered in Devon are given by Defra as: Sheep: 297,576; Cattle: 67,677; Pigs: 29,464; Goats: 112; Others: 70.

Just to give some idea of the progress of the disease monthly figures for sheep slaughtered in Devon were: February: 1,154; March: 51,836; April: 205,604; May: 27,873; June: 7,672; July: 833.

April was the cruellest month and the worst possible time. The middle of the lambing period and here comes the crunch. Many ewes were killed with lambs at foot.

Looking at Defra figures for UK as a whole from the 'Lessons to be Learned' Inquiry: The total number of animals slaughtered was 6,456,000 (i.e. nearly six and half million lives lost). In round figures 5.25 million sheep, 750,000 cattle, 500,000 pigs. That is quite a pile to incinerate or bury. This includes 'infected premises', 'dangerous contacts', 'contiguous and non-contiguous culls', 'slaughter on suspicion' and welfare cases including the 'light lamb scheme'. These figures tally with the Royal Society's, 'Infectious Diseases in Livestock' Report, 2002, which states that some six million animals were culled, plus an extra half million light lambs.

On the Defra website the cull figures for each county are given daily, which are very detailed and are highly commendable. This makes fascinating reading. However, in many people's minds the real slaughter figures may well have been much higher. To quote the Royal Society's report verbatim: 'At one stage, it was suggested that in addition to the six million animals mentioned above there could have been up to 4 million further young animals killed "at foot" (i.e. slaughtered but not counted).'

As any shepherd knows, high lambing percentages are vital for maintaining the flock. Hill flocks in Cumbria have a relatively low lambing percentage of approximately 1.2, whereas in well-kept lowland flocks this can be as high as 1.8, with an average of around 1.5. A life is a life whether it is mature, just born or as yet unborn. Many of the hill flocks lamb late and many unborn lambs were lost, i.e. they never made a mature animal. That in a sense is the true tragedy.

If there were 5.25 million sheep slaughtered, of which say 2.25 million were rams, dry sheep, barreners, tegs, two tooths, gimmers, lambs at foot etc. Then we are left with three million breeding sheep. This can be broken down into hill ewes and lowland ewes.

Say two million hill ewes with 1.2 lambs at foot $= 2 + 2 \times 1.2 = 4.4$ million sheep lives $+ 1$ million lowland ewes with 1.5 lambs at foot $= 1 + 1 \times 1.5 = 2.5$ million sheep lives, this gives an extra 3.9 million 'sheep lives' lost which should in theory be counted (i.e. a total figure of around nine million sheep lives lost, which takes the overall total to over ten million animal lives lost).

Defra however refutes these figures but cannot be absolutely certain that its own figures are 100 per cent accurate: To quote Defra directly from an email dated 28 January 2005: 'The published figures may not include all the new born lambs and calves because, for the purposes of valuing, they were counted with their mother. Work was undertaken in late 2001 on the slaughter records to assess and include the lambs and calves at foot and we believe that the final figures include most of them. However, we cannot be absolute on this. Piglets were included in the figures as they were valued separately.'

Levels of compensation were very high indeed and no doubt reflected the extra loss of lambs at foot and lambs as yet unborn. The truth no doubt lies somewhere between the two figures.

But simple arithmetic is not the only contentious issue. Vaccination is another thorny issue and significantly, although talked about and the vaccine ordered, this procedure was not in the end used. Interestingly there was a conference on FMD and Vaccination held at Bristol University on the 15th September 2001. This was led by the late Professor Fred Brown, the world expert in FMD, Ken Tyrell and two Dutch vets who had been successfully working on vaccination in the Argentine and Uruguay for the previous 20 years. (We have been importing meat from the Argentine during most of that time.) The findings and recommendations on vaccination made at the conference were very interesting and convincing. Only one government vet attended and he had been told to stay away!

Like many other shepherds I have routinely vaccinated sheep and lambs against seven or eight very nasty sounding clostridial sheep diseases including enterotoxaemia, pulpy kidney, struck, lamb dysentery, braxy, black disease, black leg and post parturient gangrene. This was administered with a single injection. There were remedies for enzootic abortion, worms, as well as sheep dip to prevent scab, a very nasty irritant mite that I have seen in several flocks. These animals thus dosed all enter the food chain and are no barrier to exports, so why should FMD vaccine be viewed any differently?

The official government line on FMD vaccination lies in the Government's new contingency plan for dealing with another outbreak which merely states that it would have to be considered. For more official information see: http://www.defra.gov.uk/animalh/diseases/fmd/disease/index.htm

However on 24th February 2005, Sir Brian Bender, Permanent Secretary to Defra, told the Commons Public Accounts Committee that the Government's preferred way of tackling an outbreak would be through vaccination as long as enough stocks of the appropriate vaccine were available. Sir Brian said the Government would try to avoid culling all animals within a three mile radius of an infected farm through effective vaccination. 'The Government does not rule out a contiguous cull, but it would not be its preferred approach. We have practical arrangements in place to be able to vaccinate within five days.'

Significantly the European Commission last year rejected a Defra claim for £960 million compensation for the cull, agreeing to pay only £350 million believing that farmers had been given pay-outs worth two to three times the true value of their slaughtered livestock. On the other hand in the proposed Animal Health Bill, the Government has 'legalised' the 'illegal' policies it carried out in 2001, and removed the right of challenging them in a court of law.

Let us hope that Foot and Mouth Disease never erupts on the same scale again and that the lessons learned are truly learnt. However, many of the lessons from the Northumberland report dealing with the earlier 1967/68 outbreak were sadly not implemented or simply ignored.

Books

Woods, Abigail (2004). *A Manufactured Plague: The History of Foot and Mouth Disease in Britain, 1839–2001*, London: Earthscan. *N.B.* This book contains the best overall bibliography on Foot and Mouth.

Whitlock, Ralph (1968). *Great Cattle Plague: An Account of the Foot and Mouth Epidemic of 1967–8*, London: John Baker.

Reports

Crisis and Opportunity: Devon Foot and Mouth Inquiry, 2001. Chaired by Professor Ian Mercer CBE.

Cumbria Foot and Mouth Disease Inquiry Report 2002. Chairman Prof Phil Thomas.

The Future of Farming and Food: Sir Don Curry 2002.

Infectious Diseases in Livestock: Sir Brian Follett Royal Society 2002.

Lessons to be Learned: Dr Iain Anderson 2002.

Defra Foot and Mouth Contingency Plan (2003) www.defra.gov.uk/footandmouth/contingency/contplan.pdf.

Articles

Alderson, Lawrence (2001) 'Foot and Mouth Disease in the United Kingdom; its Causes, Course, Control and Consequences'. *Rare Breeds International*. Paper read in Budapest 23rd August 2001.

Brown, Fred (2003). 'The History of Research Into Foot and Mouth Disease'. *Virus Research*, vol. 91, pp. 3–7.

'Carnage by Computer: The Blackboard Economics of the 2001 Foot and Mouth Report'. David Campbell and Robert Lee Cardiff Law School.

Woods, Abigail (2004). 'The Construction of an Animal Plague: Foot and Mouth Disease in Nineteenth Century Britain'. *Social History of Medicine*, vol. 17, pp. 23–39.

Woods, Abigail (2004). '"Fear and Flames on the Farm": Controlling Foot and Mouth Disease in Britain, 1892–2001'. *Historical Research*, vol. 77, pp. 520–42.

Woods, Abigail (2004). 'Keeping Britain Foot and Mouth Free: The National and International Significance of a Slaughter Policy, 1892–2001'. *Journal of Agricultural and Environmental Ethics*, vol. 17, pp. 341–62.

'Foot-and-mouth Disease as a Weapon of War and its Implications for Laboratory Research in Britain, 1924–68'. *Association of Clinical Pathologists News*, Spring 2002, pp. 13–17.

Woods, Abigail (2001). 'Foot and Mouth Disease,' in M. Sissons, ed., *A Countryside for All: The Future of Rural Britain*. London: Vintage.

For an alternative academic view of the way we interpreted FMD see:

Nerlich, B. and Döring, M. (in press). 'Poetic Justice? Rural Policy Clashes with Rural Poetry in the 2001 Outbreak of Foot and Mouth Disease in the UK'. *Journal of Rural Studies*.

Nerlich, B., Hamilton, C. and Rowe, V. (2002). 'Conceptualising Foot and Mouth Disease: The Socio-Cultural Role of Metaphors, Frames and Narratives'. *metaphorik.de*: http://www.metaphorik.de/02/nerlich.htm.

Nerlich, B (in press). '"As If Goya Was On Hand as a Marksman": Foot and Mouth Disease as a Rhetorical and Cultural Phenomenon', in I. Strecker and S.Tyler, eds., *Rhetoric Culture I: General Theory*. New York: Berghahn.

Websites

http://www.devon.gov.uk/fminquiry/finalreport/

www.defra.gov.uk

http://footandmouth.csl.gov.uk

http://www.northumberland.gov.uk/CS_FMSummary.asp

http://www.scotland.gov.uk/library5/agri/fmdr-00.asp

http://www.greenquarter.co.uk/littoral/fmd/projects.htm

www.footandmouthdoc.com

www.warmwell.com

Overleaf: Philip and Percy Lake moving a calf on the day they re-stocked, Ramscliffe Farm, Beaford, North Devon